Skincare is for life! Maisha is a powerhouse with skincare standards of the highest excellence. This book is chock-full of information that teaches you how to care for your skin the right way and put your best face forward. Her personalized skincare system is a proven blueprint for success that offers simple, effective everyday beauty regimens for different skin types and ages, along with customized tips for various skin conditions. Maisha's extensive industry expertise, inside-out approach and time-tested best practices not only positively impact the lives of her clients and team, but she also continues to help advance the careers of rising skincare professionals."

– Heather Nunley, Founder and Host of Culture Fuel Institute podcast

"Maisha truly represents Physicians Care Alliance (PCA) skin's mission of changing lives through skin care. She is a licensed, skin care professional who is passionate about skin care, helping her clients be their best selves and using the best science available to solve any skin concern. The best skin care starts in the treatment room and ends in front of the mirror at home every day. Maisha understands her client's needs and habits, therefore, she is able to offer custom, individualized advice and achieve amazing results."

– Joanna Zucker, CEO PCA skin, EltaMD and author of *Millennium Mom*

"*Skincare Always* is a delightful mix of "reference" and "reverence." "Reference" because it presents a well-organized wealth of practical knowledge about caring for skin of all types and ages. "Reverence" because of its heartfelt insight into the undeniable connection between self-respect and the health of your body and mind. I will refer to it often for both my skin care regimen and for frequent morsels of love and encouragement.

– *Lee Sheaffer, Certified Business Intermediary*

* * *

"This book is an inspiration to anyone on the journey of being the best version of themselves. We often compartmentalize life as if everything is not connected. We rarely consider how self-love impacts all areas of life, skin health being one. Maisha reflects on her personal and professional experiences and the jewels life can offer if we are willing to be open to alternative possibilities, self-exploration, reflection, vulnerability, curiosity, authenticity, and the courage not to give up. This book is a love offering of wisdom and education from a master of skin care. A practical guide to having beautiful healthy skin at every age and growing into the best version of yourself."

– *Michel Douglas-Daniels, LCSW, Licensed Clinical Therapist*

* * *

"This book is like an intimate conversation with a trusted friend. As I read it, I felt both loved and gently convicted as the author's reassuring words chided me to put and make me – my health, my self-care, my self-worth – my first priority. I highly recommend this treasured resource – chock-full of sage and solid "girlfriend" advice – to anyone interested and committed to not only obtaining and maintaining healthy, beautiful skin but to those who are ready to reaffirm that they are /we are /I am enough." – *Dr. R. Fisher*

* * *

"From reading the first few pages of this book, is the discovery that skin care is not just all about potions, serums, moisturizers and creams. Who knew that a book about skincare could put you on the road to personal fulfillment, confidence and happiness? "You glow differently when you're actually happy." Respectfully, woven throughout the pages, is great advice about your skin and the beauty within! The stories, the antidotes and most of all, Maisha Pulliam's inspiring life story is guaranteed to uplift, inspire and educate! You will "feel beautiful in your skin by starting within!"

– *San Francisco Bay Area Radio Personality, Miranda Wilson*

* * *

"*Skincare Always* is not just a skin care manual: it's a resource guide for the good life, a source of information, inspiration, encouragement, and life guidance. Maisha has infused her book with the same kind of care she offers her clients: 100% pure love. While it's loaded with details, suggestions and quick tips, the book doesn't overwhelm with facts loosely strung together around a topic. It flows with the authentic expression of a genuinely beautiful human being. Maisha's goal is clear: to help people become their best selves. Among the many tips offered, Maisha suggests considerations in finding the perfect aesthetician. Here's my tip: you've found her. Maisha is the best!"

— Victoria Theodore, pianist / singer / music director/ composer / educator known for touring and recording with Stevie Wonder, Beyoncé, Chloe+Halle, Broadway and more...

* * *

"This book was so powerful, and so much more than just about skin. It was uplifting, positive, and very informational. It also promoted self-love and acceptance and being happy in the skin you're in. This book is for everyone, with good skin and not so good skin. I was so inspired; I immediately washed my face and made a commitment to wash day and night and to be more intentional with my skin care regimen." *–Tracy Jones, UCSF Customer service representative*

* * *

"*Skincare Always* was very empowering, not only was it about skincare but also taking care of your body, mind and spirit. I liked that it had tips for all skin types and different age groups. After reading the book, I gave up coffee and committed to washing my face twice daily instead of just the mornings. Skincare Always should be read by every man, woman, boy and girl to ensure that have beautiful skin always."

– Stacy Jones, John Muir Collections specialist

* * *

"It is hard to describe everything an esthetician is to her clients. However, this book shows that Maisha is everything an esthetician should be and more. Maisha's dedication to her craft and the care she provides to her clients is nothing short of extraordinary. She thrives off of helping others find their best selves, starting with skin care, always. This book details her philosophy around caring for your skin and ultimately yourself. Reading this will help make skin care easier for you and take you through a journey of caring for your skin through all of its stages.

– *Annie Diaz, National Sales Director of PCA Skin and Licensed Esthetician*

SKINCARE ALWAYS

FEEL BEAUTIFUL IN YOUR SKIN, STARTING WITHIN

MAISHA PULLIAM

EARTH AND SOUL PUBLISHING, INC.

ISBN: 978-0-578-98378-3 (paperback)

ISBN: 978-0-578-30898-2 (hardback)

Editor: Diane Riis

Book cover design: Andrea Schmidt

Photography: Jennifer Graham Photography

DEDICATION

To my daughter, best friend, right hand, and business manager, Blaique Yvonnea. You wear so many hats! I dedicate this book to you. You are the wind beneath my wings. I tell you the story from time to time that when I was pregnant with you, I would rub my belly and tell you that with you, Mommy could do anything. I truly felt you had given me superpowers and you did. Every single thing I have accomplished is because of you, my beautiful daughter. You are my reason. I never fought so hard in my life for anything until you. You made me feel so deserving of any and everything I wanted. I felt if God could bless me with such a beautiful little baby and trust me to care for this precious human, there was nothing I couldn't do and nothing God wouldn't give me. As you grew older, you challenged me to live that truth and I have. Every day I look at you, you remind me that I am strong, capable, and deserving because I raised a woman that I one day hope to be! You are the strongest, most loving, loyal, dedicated, focused, giving, honest, hardworking, smartest, funniest (and the list goes on) person I know. I am so proud to be working beside you daily. I am so glad this parenting thing transitioned into the most beautiful friendship I have ever had. I couldn't do any of this without you, my love. Thank you for all your dedication and long hours of working so I could work on this book dream and make it a reality. Mommy is so incredibly proud of the woman you have become and the woman you are becoming. I wish you a lifetime of over-the-moon success, happiness, peace, and joy because that is what you add to every life you touch!

CONTENTS

INTRODUCTION

If you take care of your skin, it's sure to look like you do.
—Maisha

Hello, Beautiful!

This book is a resource for you at any age. No matter how old you are, I suggest you read every chapter as this book is about where you've been as well as where you're going. You will find tips to care for your skin that you may have missed at an earlier age, but you can apply them now—it's not too late! You will also learn what to prepare for in your future.

Your skin deserves all the attention you can give it. It is neither self-absorbed nor conceited to make your skin and beauty a priority. In fact, I believe it is your responsibility. As you are empowered to love the skin you are in, you empower other women to do the same. It truly is contagious. I want to share the gift of skin care with the world! Maybe you will do the same, but first, share it with the most important person walking this earth...you!

Before I take you on a journey through the decades helping you see how prevention, self-care, and dedication will guarantee you beautiful skin for the rest of your life, I will start with a chapter that applies to women at any age. I will go into detail about skin types and some of the biggest concerns I see: acne, hyperpigmentation, and allergy-related skin conditions.

In addition to my tips and advice for every age, I've included information for parents of tweens and teens. Skin care is one of the best gifts we can offer to our friends and loved ones. By giving your tween or teen the gift of skin care, you give them the gift of self-care, which will stay with them for the rest of their lives.

The Gift of Skin Care

My goal is to share not just my love for skin care but also the things I have learned over the years. For the past twenty-one years, I have had the opportunity to work with thousands of faces and have watched transformational improvements through the treatments I offer. I want to share my advice with you along with the skincare products and tips I have recommended to my clients. I will share stories from the women I have worked with as well as my own observations from my life journey.

I have worked with young children from ten years old to adults in their eighties and beyond. I have seen what amazing changes skin care can make right before my eyes. I've also witnessed the difference that positive reinforcement, believing in oneself, and increasing self-love can make in someone's life.

In addition to skincare advice and supporting women to be their very best, I have given advice on how diet and lifestyle can improve the appearance and health of the skin. I am proud to say almost every client I have worked with that has decided to follow my advice has gotten the results they were seeking. It is so helpful to have tools like these to use not just for yourself but also to help someone else along their skincare journey. It is our duty as lovers of skin! I hope you find this information as useful as my clients do. Skin care always!

About Me (and You)

For as long as I can remember I have loved skin and anything related to beauty. But as a student of life, I have been most fascinated with learning about people, to hear what interests them and what their stories are. I love to serve and help others as well. I always have. Watching someone grow and achieve their personal and professional goals fills my heart beyond words. This is my life's calling: to help women achieve every goal they set for themselves, from beautiful skin to self-love. This book is about skin care, yes, but so much more.

Since my calling in life is bigger than just helping women with their appearance, I have never felt that telling people I am an esthetician is an accurate description of all that I do. If I leave it at that, I know intuitively I am short-changing myself. Have you ever felt that way? You share what you do, and you see a blank stare, and you know they're thinking,

"Oh, is that all?"

You want to say, "Actually, I do so much more," but for whatever reason, you just leave well enough alone. You are left thinking, "What more am I? What more do I offer?"

Yes, I have been there far too often, which is why I thought a lot about what I really do for the women I work with. Obviously, I treat the skin. I help heal and pamper the skin and educate my clients about how to care for their skin and so on. That, in my opinion, is quite a bit. But I offer so much more.

Many people will jokingly say that their esthetician is also their life coach or therapist. When my clients said that of me, I used to brush it off as a joke. I was simply doing my job. However, as I began to really look at what my vocation is, I discovered that this is my calling. Skin is my work and my career, and I am incredibly passionate about it and gifted at it. However, I am even more passionate about the life and wellbeing of the person I am working with, well beyond skin care. I am passionate about their dreams, aspirations, goals, celebrations, and challenges. I am driven to dig deeper and help those I meet find resources to learn to heal, to work through difficult challenges, and to push to higher greatness. Honestly, when I am working with women, this all comes together with skin, and it always has for me.

I am clear that I am not a psychotherapist. I am speaking of supporting women in a positive, effective way, the same way many women have done for me. Had I not had strong, wise, loving, supportive mentors in my life, I certainly would not be where I am now. So, today, I am that for others. I hope I can be that for you.

I am deeply passionate about helping women obtain personal, professional, and financial success and, most importantly, freedom. I know to have this, a deep sense of self-worth and purpose must be discovered, and this is the work I commit to daily for myself, and I try to help others do the same.

I enjoy seeing my clients grow inwardly as well as outwardly. It is important for women to see the beauty within first and then match their outer with their inner. I know this takes work, and the journey is different for everyone.

With respect to skin, I learned early in my career that though a group of women may all have the same issues such as acne, rosacea, melasma, eczema, or psoriasis, they each have their own individual concerns and sensitivities as well. So I don't work with my clients as a group but rather as individuals, learning their skin and skin needs specifically. This calls for me to also customize their treatment application, home care, and how I advise them and work with them overall. This customization helps my clients gain success and fast.

Skincare Survival Skills

I work with women (and men) suffering from skin issues or concerns, those looking to reverse or slow down signs of aging, as well as with women who just want to relax and have their skin pampered. I study my client's skin and help them understand it as I see it. Then I mix and create personalized concoctions using professional pharmaceutical-grade products and ingredients from the manufacturers I have partnered with.

I've been doing this since I was a child. I remember watching old movies and seeing women getting facials. I would go into the kitchen and use whatever we had on hand to make a mask for myself. I can't begin to tell you why my hand reached for certain things like lemons, milk, mayonnaise, oatmeal, brown sugar, and baking soda from the kitchen or even witch hazel, alcohol, Campho-Phenique, calamine lotion, or Philips Milk of Magnesia from the bathroom cabinet. I suppose I studied the consistency, texture, smell, and feel of things, and I still do.

I was incredibly lucky because my grandmother had everything you can possibly imagine in the house or in her garden. It was heaven for my curious and adventurous soul. When my acne started in about the fifth or sixth grade, my focus became acne, and I would pull out anything I could from the kitchen or medicine cabinet to create something to heal my skin and take the acne away. I had some wins but also had many moments of making matters worse, which is how I learned early on what a big impact a product can have on the skin. This was the foundation I built on. I was a "mad scientist" in the most natural way for me—making potions, lotions, and treatments. I call these "skincare survival skills." I tell people often if there ever comes a time that we don't have access to skincare products, I can literally go into the woods and make something from the earth for your skin. So if we are ever lost in the wilderness, I won't be able to build a fire or save you from the lion, tiger, or bear, but your skin will be in great hands!

It is this innate gift that speaks to me and tells me what is going on with someone's skin. It tells me what to mix and blend and how to use it best. It is pretty awesome. For a long time, I was not even aware of the gift. It came so naturally to me that I did not pay much attention to it. Once I really started working with clients and focusing on how to best care for them, especially when traditional skincare methods were not helping, I began to go within for guidance. The skin would speak to me, and I would speak back. Not audibly, but quietly within. Today, I still do this. It never fails; the skin always speaks to me. We have quite a connection for which I am grateful. Certainly, I have trained formally and continue to do so, as I believe in continuing education. However, the intuitive practice is equally important to me because it lets me truly specialize in customization, which is a vital part of my practice.

See the Beauty in You

I know being challenged with a skin condition can be frustrating and even defeating. However, I want to encourage you to speak positive words to your skin condition and yourself. That's exactly what I am doing when I work with clients. Yes, there is a time for gentle consolation and a time to "give it to you straight," but we all know tough love is often necessary when trying to combat our toughest challenges. I would like to think I find a balance with both gentleness and discipline. So serving as an accountability coach for my clients, I require that they exercise discipline in the quest for both physical and emotional good health—as a means to be at peace and to find happiness in addition to uncovering beautiful, healthy skin. Some of what I tell you in this book might sound like "tough love," but I am going to "give it to you straight," just like I would if you came into my skincare studio.

The Beauty of My Calling

I mentioned that I have been fascinated with beauty and all things related from an early age. I knew about dermatology, but I didn't know helping people with the esthetics of their skin was a profession. I didn't know it was a "thing." But one day I went and got a facial, and when the lady touched my face, I knew that it was what I was supposed to do, and my journey began. I was already doing it innately my whole life, but I didn't know it was a career. At the time, I had been praying and trying to figure out my purpose in life, my gift, my calling, and it came to me in my sleep. God said, "Go find a school..."

Now my passion allows me to share sound advice, products, and services to help my clients care for their skin and look and feel their best. I educate women about the importance of patience, perseverance, diligence, and the application of the correct products. Knowing that I have improved someone's life by assisting them in returning their skin closer to what they were born with has made my journey so worthwhile.

I hope you find the answers to your skincare concerns, but even more, I hope you find inspiration for your journey.

There is no such thing as perfect. Embrace your imperfections and work on anything that has room for improvement. —Maisha

1

SKIN CARE ALWAYS

Isn't it the time to look and feel great? —Maisha

I have dedicated most of my life to beauty, as this passion started when I was a young child. I would study my grandmother, and I remember asking her when she first noticed specific signs of aging on her face and body. I think she was somewhat annoyed with my constant questions. "Girl, I don't think about that stuff!" she'd say with a swatting motion of her hand. She always sounded gentle and humorous but also frustrated when I kept drilling.

"How can you not think about that?" I would ask. "How can you not look at yourself and see the changes, Nanny?"

"Girl, you just get older, and the changes just happen," she'd answer.

I would stare at her for hours noticing her beauty, as well as the aging impressions that had made a home on her beautiful face, neck, décolleté, arms, hands, legs, and feet. Even as a child, I intuitively knew the aging process couldn't be prevented completely; however, I intuitively knew there must be something to slow it down and encourage the aging process to happen more gracefully.

What My Mom Gave Me

My mother was a different story. She was a young mother, only seventeen years old when she had me. When I was with my mom, I spent a great deal of time admiring her beauty as well. I would watch when I thought she wasn't looking because if she noticed, she'd say, "Girl, why are you staring at me like that?"

I really could not explain why. I just had this thing with faces, and I wanted to study them. The only time I could really get in some good staring time with her was when my mother was "doing her face," as she would call it, when she was applying her makeup or doing her skincare routine. She had flaw-less, beautiful, brown, smooth skin that always glowed. She was a natural beauty. The only makeup she wore was eyeliner, mascara, and red-burgundy lipstick. Boy, could my mother wear some eyeliner and mascara. She had a technique that made her already beautiful big eyes just look like glimmery jewels.

My mother was different from my grandmother in that she was intentional about her skin. She used Neutrogena soap and Avon products which included different potions and lotions she would apply to her skin. I remember it being very simple, but my point is she did do something.

It worked to an extent. Today, I always tell my clients that doing something with your skin, even something small, is better than doing nothing at all. Of course, it's important to be sure that the prod-ucts you choose, even if simple and basic, are ideal for your skin type. My mother's skin always stayed pretty nice. I know that had she used the products that I am aware of today, her skin would have looked even more youthful and healthy. In fact, before she left this earth, I would care for her skin, and she loved it. She would always say, "Now, Maisha, you know I have always taken care of my skin."

I would reply, "Yes, Mama, you always did. That's why you look so good."

I knew that was what she really wanted to hear, and no matter what, she will always be the prettiest woman in the world to me.

My grandmother and the other women in my family have been lucky to have amazing genetics working in their favor. But genetics alone won't preserve the youthful appearance and health of your skin forever. It takes intention. It takes invested time, money, a great esthetician, advanced skincare products, patience, and implementing the correct skincare practices with discipline and consistency.

You Are Worth It

Most women want to look good and feel good. However, I notice many women aren't willing to do the work. When I ask why, they say they don't have the time, they don't have the money, or they have used so many different products that haven't proven to be effective, they don't trust skin care. I always work with my clients to first make a mind shift. Skin care does make a difference. You do have the time. We all make time for what is important to us. Is your skin important to you? Are you important? The answer is always, "yes."

You have the money. You have a job; you pay for the things you want. Think about the dinners, the outings, the clothes, the perfume you purchase for yourself. It's about prioritizing. Is your skin a priority? The answer is always, "yes."

In the cases when products didn't work for you, likely you used the wrong product. Either you self-selected or you got advice from someone that didn't specialize in your skin type or mis-assessed your skin type. It happens. Don't give up because one or several experiences don't prove to be the perfect fit. How many times have you purchased shoes, pants, skirts, shirts, or perfume and when you got home discovered it wasn't the fit you thought? So you return for a better fit until you nail it. How many times have you gotten an eyeglass prescription or medication prescription and had to get adjustments? It happens. The point is, leave some room for trial and error when it comes to skin care. It's worth it to discover what's perfect for you. And hey, just like doctors, estheticians aren't psychics or mind readers. Sometimes it's necessary to see how the skin and body respond in order to pair you with the perfect skincare system.

Generally, matching a client with a perfect skincare system is seamless; however, there are times, for example if you have hypersensitive skin, that it is necessary to makes changes and modifications along the way. With time, we change; our skincare needs might change as well. So we need to modify once again. That's natural and to be expected. So listen, let's make an agreement right now...you are worth it!

Find Your Superpower Within

I would like to go a little deeper than talking about your skin for a minute. Hopefully, you've decided what self-worth means to you, what it looks like, and how to embrace it. It took me years to fall in love with myself and celebrate me, and I still work on this piece daily. It's not a "one and done," which is something I learned in therapy some years ago. I would ask my therapist,

"Okay, when will I be fixed? I have things to get to, and this is taking too much time."

She would laugh and say, "Maisha, the rest of your life, that's how long it takes. The true work on ourselves never stops."

If you are anything like me, you may think something is seriously wrong with you if you have to spend the rest of your life working on yourself. Just like you will keep investing time and effort in your skin care, you must on yourself.

But I learned working on me is a gift I give myself daily. I encourage you to do that as well. You may never go to therapy, but you can still choose to make working on yourself a daily, true, intentional act. I could cry thinking about the days I didn't have time for me, wanting to rush me. But I had all the time in the world for so many other people and things that were so much less important.

Because of the effort, time, and struggles it has taken to understand, change, and embrace all the parts of me, it is so important to me that every woman knows her worth. It's not something you need to chase either. It's built within you. It's right with you wherever you are. The challenge is to recognize and know your worth so you can survive and thrive. The same way I know instinctively that your skin can thrive and be beautiful, I know that you can too.

I want you to know you are beautiful, no matter your color, race, background, struggles, or anything else that makes you, *you*. You are capable, loved, valued, significant, and even in times of feeling vulnerable, doubtful, and weak, you are still beautiful. You are still enough! No matter what happens to you or around you, those are parts of you that never change.

When we learn the real "secret" and embrace the truth that we are capable, loved, valued, significant, and beautiful, it is easier to embrace and accept even more wonderful things about ourselves. You know, the things that make you unique. Me, for example? I am a neat freak, incredibly clean and organized, which can drive some people crazy, and it has. But this is who I am; it's how I am wired; even if I wanted to change it, I really don't think I could.

I love to help people by giving advice. I'm incredibly opinionated. There are social conversations I prefer to engage in and even music I prefer. I love luxury, a certain style of dress, and so on. These are some of the things that make me, me. I am strong; I don't give up easily once I have set my mind to it, and if I do give up, trust me, my claw prints are truly engraved in that thing.

I am loyal; I don't like to argue, which might make me appear passive when really, it's that I love peace and I love love.

There was a time I thought all these things made me weak, difficult, unlovable, and unworthy of what I really wanted. Today, these are the things I value the most. Now I know when we find value in ourselves, we discover our worth.

Once I realized I needed to embrace the things I couldn't change, once I freed myself from the negative thoughts of what I wasn't or couldn't be, I was free to be myself. I turned these "negatives" into my affirmations. I recommend you do the same.

For example, you might say, "I am stingy with my things." But what if you rephrased it as, "I value my things and am very protective of them." Then, if it's true, embrace it.

Sure, we all have things we need to change, but you be the judge. Take some time alone and list all the things you wish to change about yourself. Looking at that list, what are the things you know deep down you cannot change? Write them down. Ask yourself whether they are truly that bad, or are they things that make other people uncomfortable? Perhaps it's about changing the company you keep.

If there are things you realize you want to change, be gentle with yourself. Start with one thing and be patient. Move on to the next thing when you're ready. You will see yourself blossoming in no time. It is important to take note of these beautiful changes inwardly and outwardly. As you collect these love notes to yourself, they become reminders about your choices and your self-worth. People call these notes affirmations or mantras. Call them whatever you would like. As long as you find a way to remind yourself often that you are worthy. Let your self-worth be your superpower.

Maybe you will look at your life and decide you don't need to change anything. I hear many women say, "I wish I could get dressed up daily, do my hair, makeup, and dress, but instead, I look like a bum," which is always an exaggerated statement. Listen, if this is you and you really wish to change this, change it. But if you are comfortable in athletic wear (which is not a bad thing), accept that about yourself. Try affirming, "I dress to produce my best! Athletic wear allows me to move in a way that makes me feel most comfortable. If I want to dress up, I can easily do it."

I want to drive this home because I feel so strongly about it. You must be willing to accept, embrace, and affirm the things that make you, you. You are worthy of all things just because you are, period. When you do this, you will discover your self-worth, and before you can come into your power, you must recognize it for yourself.

There is no such thing as flawless. Accept being beautifully, perfectly, and wonderfully flawed.

—Maisha

2

SKIN CARE FOR ALL

Self-care is skin care. −Maisha

What's Uber Important to Know

Before I get into skin at different ages and stages, I wanted to include some information that is useful for everyone. Taking care of these four things will improve the condition of your skin no matter how old you are.

First, prioritize your skin with daily care. Establish a routine and stick with it. It is vital to the health of your skin to have a morning and evening skincare routine that you stick to. No matter how early or rushed you are in the morning. No matter how late you get home at night. No matter how tired, stressed, or depressed you are. Not even if you feel your skin looks "the bomb"! Absolutely no skipping your skin care regimen. No sleeping in makeup or working out in makeup either. Try to be makeup free as often as possible to allow your skin to breathe.

Second, I tell everybody they must understand their skin type and know how to care for it properly. There are often things you need to add to your skin-care regimen and diet, and there are things you may need to avoid.

Third, supplying your skin with essential, active, and effective ingredients is key for your skin to thrive. I often see people using products they just pulled off the shelf, but the products have no real benefits, and therefore they gain no success in trying to correct or improve their skin, let alone preserve its health. It is important to use pharmaceutical-grade products from reputable brands that blend science and nature within their formulations. A sunscreen with SPF should *always* be part of your daily skin care, no matter your age or skin color. The sun is incredibly damaging to all skin and causes it to age faster than anything, so you must protect it every day.

And fourth, getting a regular (monthly) facial will help support the health of your skin with a professional exfoliation, which aids in increasing cellular turnover. This increases collagen and elastin production to keep the skin firmer for years to come. It also helps cleanse the pores, reduces discoloration, supports an even complexion, smooths texture, and gives skin a healthy glow on an advanced level.

Skin Types

Since skin type is such an important topic, I want to give it the attention it deserves. I recommend everyone seek professional advice to take the guesswork out of skin care and to get a system that is perfect and customized just for you. An esthetician will help you identify and address your specific concerns. Keep in mind that what I provide here are guidelines to get you started and not everyone will "fit" into the categories. Understanding your skin type and selecting the correct products are key to your skincare success. Without these two components, your skin is likely struggling to thrive and maintain a youthful, healthy glow.

People generally misdiagnose their skin, thinking they have oily or combination skin when what I see most is skin that is dry and/or sensitive because of allergies. I constantly tell people that just because you see a shine does not mean you're oily. Most people are not oily, and those who think they are actually have dry and sensitive skin, as well as allergies. When their allergies are flared up, the skin does not retain moisture because the skin is compromised. Once allergies are controlled, the skin normalizes, and the dryness is alleviated. The skin is then able to retain moisture, and one can experience healthy, hydrated skin.

Why the Skin Type Hype?

Knowing your skin type is key to selecting the correct formulations and routine for you. But even once you know your skin type, you have to avoid assumptions about what works. For example, having oily skin doesn't mean avoiding a moisturizer, and dry skin doesn't mean you should use petroleum jelly. When people misdiagnose their skin type, they don't choose the products that are best for them. If you aren't using the ideal products for your skin, you won't get the results you are looking for.

There are four textbook skin types: normal, dry, oily, and combination. I include sensitive and hypersensitive skin types because I see them often with my clients. I am going to start with dry skin because, in my opinion, it is the most common skin type.

Dry Skin

You might have dry skin if...

You experience flakiness.

Your skin feels tight right after you cleanse.

You have an ashy or chalky appearance.

Your skin feels itchy with no fine bumps.

Your skin appears oily, but you still feel tight and dry.

You have a dry, raw texture around the creases of the nose.

Your mouth area has a dry and dark appearance.

Your eyebrows are dry and flaky.

Your scalp is dry and flaky.

You are in your twenties and thirties and you have fine lines on various areas of your face.

Not many people think they're dry, so when I tell them they are, they're surprised. In general, dry and sensitive skin is what I see the most. If your skin feels tight or dry after cleansing, you have flaking or itchy skin, or you constantly feel the need to apply a heavier moisturizer, you might have dry skin.

When I look at dry skin, I see a lackluster appearance, discoloration, and crepey-ness. I might notice the skin has a grayish tone. The skin doesn't look lively; there's no glow to it. I compare it to a plant that needs watering. When a plant begins to wilt, you can tell it's struggling; it sags, its leaves don't shine, they aren't vibrant. When you water it, it wakes up, the leaves perk up; the color perks up. It's the same with the skin. When skin is hydrated, it wakes up.

Often dry skin is due to cleansers that are drying and moisturizers that are not hydrating enough. Other common causes are air conditioners, fans pointing directly at your face, cleansing with hot or hard water, using harsh laundry detergents, or fabric softeners.

Oftentimes people think drinking water will resolve the problem, and, yes, you want to drink water, but it is not the remedy for dry skin. If you're doing the wrong things in terms of what you eat or drink, or you use products that flare up allergies, you aren't going to resolve the problem by drinking water. You will solve the problem by avoiding what is flaring up your allergy and causing your skin to be dry. If you have allergies to things like caffeine, dairy, dairy substitutes, fabric softeners, and dyes, which are very common, it is going to flare up and cause your skin to be drier and more sensitive. When people eliminate those things from their life, their skin balances. Those are things we can control. Other allergens like pollen, trees, cats, dogs, we can't.

Understanding Why You Are Dry and Oily

To hydrate dry skin, the body has to be in a healed mode, and when it's not, it constantly uses its water. The water evaporates instead of being retained within the epidermis. This is called transepidermal water loss. It's what you experience when you over-stimulate oil due to lack of hydration or possibly allergies. When the skin is dry and the epidermis cannot retain moisture, the oil glands (sebaceous glands) will produce oil to supply the skin with lubrication. They overstimulate, causing you to be super-ficially oily. Our body is designed to self-lubricate the eyes, the joints; that's how we are designed. So because we're so dry, signals are sent to the glands that we need moisture. Our oil glands will then overproduce sebum (oil), causing superficial oiliness, but the skin is still dry. If allergies are controlled by avoiding certain foods and using better products for your skin type, your skin balances out and signals to the glands to stop producing all this oil. The skin says, "I'm fine now! Now I can retain water; I don't need your help anymore!" That's how we find balance.

Caring for Dry Skin

One of the most frustrating things for people with dry skin is that they feel like they can't put on enough moisture. But it is possible to control dry skin so you can feel hydrated and balanced and ditch that dry-tight feeling. Make these changes, and likely you will see and feel more hydrated skin!

1. Drink plenty of water (because it doesn't help not to.)
2. Make sure to avoid caffeine, dairy, and dairy replacements.
3. Avoid fabric softeners, dryer sheets, and liquid softeners.
4. Cleanse the skin with tepid water, not hot, which will dry the skin out.
5. Cleanse with a gentle cleanser that is not stripping.
6. Use a hydrating toner after cleansing.
7. Make sure you use hydrating serums containing ingredients like hyaluronic acid, vitamin C, and niacinamide.
8. Moisturize morning and night.
9. Use an SPF daily.
10. Avoid having heaters or fans blow directly in your face.

Oily Skin

You might have oily skin if...

You have large pores.

You become oily within a few hours of cleansing your skin.

Your skin is always overly shiny.

Your pores are consistently clogged.

If your skin is always shiny and collects oil shortly after washing your face and/or you have larger pores and are typically prone to acne, you may have oily skin. But most people think they're oily when they're not. A major tip...just because you have acne, does not mean you are oily. Just because your skin is shiny does not mean you have oily skin. Generally speaking, most of the time, people who think they have oily skin actually have dry and sensitive skin. They have allergies, and when those allergies are flared up, their skin is not retaining moisture. Before your skin can retain moisture, it needs to heal, as I discussed.

Controlling Oily Skin

One of the most frustrating things for women and men is an oily, overly shiny face. Controlling oily skin takes some implemented adjustments, but it is possible. Selecting the proper skincare products for your skin type, diet, and lifestyle definitely plays a role. Here are some tips to keep that oil at bay.

1. Cleanse skin with cool water. Heat stimulates oil production.
2. Do not over-cleanse or strip the skin. This also causes the glands to stimulate more oil production.
3. Use a lightweight moisturizer for oily skin.
4. Do not skip using a moisturizer because you think you are oily enough. This actually makes you oilier. Use a moisturizer day and night.
5. Drink plenty of water to keep skin hydrated so it can depend less on the body's natural oil for moisture.
6. Reduce dairy, fried, and salty foods.
7. When wearing SPF or makeup, use an oil free formulation.

I generally recommend products like foaming cleansers, gel serums, and light, oil-free moisturizers for an oily skin type. These products definitely work best.

Normal Skin

You might have normal skin if...

Your skin is not dry or oily.

Your skin feels and looks balanced with no indication of oiliness or dryness or any sensitivities.

You have no complaints with your skin.

If you have normal skin, likely you have no complaints. You are definitely one of the lucky ones! Skin still ages no matter how lucky you are, so it will behoove you to still care for your skin by having a morning and night routine consisting of your essential homecare products: cleanser, toner, serums, moisturizer, and an SPF. It is also important to get monthly professional facials to maintain your healthy skin for years to come.

Sensitive and Hypersensitive Skin

You might have sensitive skin if...

You experience irritation.

Your skin is dry.

You see redness.

You have fine bumps or a rash.

Everything you use tends to irritate your skin.

You experience burning, stinging, itching, or your skin feels hot.

You have patches of redness, dryness, or flaking.

If you often have redness, inflammation, irritation, or most things burn and cause a reaction, you might have sensitive or even hypersensitive skin. You want to make sure you're using products that are hydrating and soothing. We want to focus on niacinamide, which is very healing, as well as vitamin C, which is also very healing as are many other antioxidants. However, products that are too stimulating will cause irritation, so they should be avoided. Other things that can cause sensitivity include:

- Sun
- Heat from a sauna/steam room/shower
- Aggressive topical skincare products that may be too stimulating
- Aggressive exfoliation/scrubbing
- Stress
- Medications

Some Simple Tips for Sensitive and Hypersensitive Skin

1. Gentle cleansing with a creamy cleanser
2. Avoiding harsh, stripping products and aggressive exfoliation
3. Avoiding products that are too stimulating
4. Using hydrating serums, rich moisturizers, or balms

Combination Skin

You might have combination skin if...

Your T-zone area is oily and the other areas of your face are dry.

Your T-zone area is dry and the other areas of your face are oily.

It is said that if you have an oily T-zone (forehead, nose and chin) and the other areas of your face are dry or vice versa, you have combination skin. I don't agree with this theory though it would appear to be combination skin. I believe if you have dry areas on your face, you fall under the dry skin category. As I mentioned earlier, the reason for an oily T-zone with dry areas elsewhere on your face is that the sebaceous glands are stimulated and over-producing oil due to lack of water. Technically you have dry skin in my opinion, and should it be treated as such.

All in all, understanding your skin type in depth will help you care for it properly. Always choose the correct products, diet, and lifestyle to support your skin. It's important; it's your face!

Should I Use a Retinol?

Gone are the days of having to deal with the constant irritation of Retin-A, which was once the way to reduce wrinkles and aging as well as acne and discoloration. Some of the leading skincare companies have developed retinols in various formulations to deliver gentle, yet drastic results. This can be achieved with no downtime, regardless of your skin type. Retinols were developed to speed up cellular turnover to exfoliate, stimulate collagen and elastin, fight acne, and clear discoloration. Retinols are powerful antioxidants, but, especially for sensitive skin, it is important to use them in the proper way.

If you have never used retinol before, you should use with caution and allow your skin time to acclimate slowly. I recommend when first beginning to use retinol, use it every three nights for two weeks, then every two nights for two weeks, then every night. This allows the skin to acclimate well.

Step 1: Wash your face.

Step 2: Tone.

Step 3: Wait a few minutes until your skin is completely dry. This is important because if your skin is at all damp, the retinol will be able to absorb more deeply into your skin and might cause irritation. We want to apply moisturizers and most serums to slightly damp skin, but never retinol. Serums that contain acids like salicylic, glycolic, and lactic may also be too stimulating for sensitive skin if used while skin is still damp.

Step 4: Take a pea-size amount of your retinol, and starting at your chin, apply with your fingertips in upward and outward motions. If you have other serums, cocktail them all together with your retinol. No need to separate them.

Step 5: Apply eye cream. An eye cream will help protect the delicate skin around your eyes.

Step 6: Finish with your moisturizer.

Step 7: Remember to apply a broad-spectrum sunscreen the morning after as retinol makes skin more sensitive to the sun.

Your skin is a reflection of your choices. —Maisha

Glowing skin is always in. –Maisha

3

_____

ACNE-PRONE SKIN

Optimism is necessary to gain the results you desire.
—Maisha

A cne is a condition that can be most
challenging to control; however, if you
understand what is causing your breakouts (getting
to the root of the problem), you can most certainly
control it. I hear from many of my clients that they
feel they are breaking out because of their menstrual
cycle, stress, birth control, and many other things.
Though there may be some truth to it, in most
cases, I challenge my clients to consider those
things may not be the cause. I give them a list of
likely acne culprits they should avoid, and I provide

a healthier skincare routine to practice, including products I recommend, and guess who clears up? That's right, my clients do! See, when you are struggling with acne, yes, your menstrual cycle, stress, and birth control can contribute to the breakouts, but it's likely because you are already exposing yourself to many of the acne culprits. I don't believe our menstrual cycle alone causes acne, but if you are taking in too much dairy and salt during that time of month, it absolutely can. I don't believe stress alone causes acne, but if you are doing things that cause acne because of stress, it will definitely cause you to break out. Generally, while under stress, we can start eating poorly, stop caring for our skin properly, use the wrong hair products, not wash our hair as frequently, and so on. Does that make sense? That makes stress a big acne culprit.

The Nature of Acne

The difference between someone with acne versus someone without acne is how active or inactive the P.acnes bacteria are within their oil glands. For oilier skin, the bacteria tends to be more active and easily stimulated, which causes breakouts. For drier skin types, the glands produce less oil, so there are usually fewer breakouts. P.acnes bacteria is naturally-occurring, but in some people, it's more stimulated than in others. When this is the case, things like your cell phone touching your face, eating dairy or salty foods, oily hair products, and such will cause you to break out immediately. In teenagers, the bacteria is often very active, but as the oil glands shrink with age, the acne will subside because the oil glands will begin to produce less oil. Acne can and will occur at any age, but the less active the bacteria and oil glands, the more difficult it is to break out. The goal is always to avoid the things that cause acne, and I have added a list of known culprits at the end of this chapter to help you out.

Allergies, Sensitivities, and Acne

Using acne products is fine, but I ask what are you doing that's stimulating the breakout? Is it dairy, which is an inflammatory food and stimulates the P. Acnes bacteria? Or are you using fabric softeners that make your clothes smell good and feel soft but transfer to your skin and clog pores? Are you using hair or lip products when you sleep or wearing makeup? Maybe your husband, wife, boyfriend, or girlfriend uses beard oil or gels, and you're hugging him or her. All these things can cause acne. I've even seen certain multivitamins, which are poorly sourced or have too much biotin, stimulate acne too; they affect your hormones. My theory is when these things go into the body, it causes the P. acnes bacteria to be stimulated. This is what I see: acne never just happens. We might be prone to acne because of P. acnes bacteria and hormones, but the products we use and foods we choose stimulate it. When people stop using these things, their acne clears.

Many of us underestimate the impact our environment and diet have on our skin, so if you are experiencing skin that isn't ideal, common triggers to certain foods and household products might be the culprit. Those are things we can do something about, and it starts with avoiding common triggers.

Culprits to Avoid to Reduce Acne

- Cheese
- Dairy
- Detergents: All & Gain (recommend Tide, no softener)
- Dryer sheets
- Fabric softeners
- Face picking
- Ice cream
- Peanuts
- Perfume (avoid face & shoulders)
- Protein shakes
- Soy products
- Sour cream
- Tissues infused with lotions

- Petroleum jelly
- Certain vitamins or supplements
- Hair gels, oils, sprays (recommend shampoo and conditioner only)

Keep in mind, acne is complicated, and that's why a consultation is important. I drill people with questions. There's no cure, but it can be controlled.

Client Success Story: Jackie

Jackie P., twenty-three, came in not only with acne and scarring, but she was also incredibly sensitive. She complained that she was experiencing irritation, and everything she put on her face was burning. Her skin was very inflamed: red, hot, and dry with cystic acne, comedones, and pus-filled acne. After our consultation, I sensed her passion and determination to clear up. It moved me, as I related to once having acne and feeling so lost yet desperate for a solution, constantly using the wrong products, making matters worse. This is an area of skin care that I am very passionate about. I am always committed to doing whatever it takes to help my clients clear up. I began Jackie's treatment, and even the gentle cleanser I used on her skin caused her skin to feel a burning sensation. I explained to her that her skin was compromised by her allergies which were currently flared up. Once she changed her diet, removing all caffeine, dairy, dairy replacements, and fabric softeners as well as detergents with dyes and fragrances, her skin would normalize.

I had Jackie start on a simple, homecare skin system. Because she didn't have the budget for my full skincare system, she got her basic essentials which included her brightening cleanser, brightening and hydrating toner, moisturizing treatment, and a sunscreen. I sent her home with her list of things to avoid as well. After a few treatment visits and consultations, Jackie's skin began to normalize and clear. It took Jackie some time to make all the changes necessary to clear up completely. But seeing is believing. Once she saw improvement, she then trusted me to do every single thing I suggested for her to do, and she cleared up. Eventually Jackie was able to invest more in her skin, allowing her to get more products for home care and advanced treatments, which gained her even better results and now is facing the world confidently with clear, radiant skin.

Jackie always commented that although her skin was broken out, she still knew she was beautiful. I loved how she spoke very highly of herself. She would also say she wanted to clear her skin to feel even better about herself. She hated her breakouts. She set her intentions, and Jackie made it happen. I am so proud of her! She is a testament to how discipline, patience, implementation, and consistency will allow you to achieve your goals!

Basic Rules to Avoid Acne

We hate rules, and often we break them, but your choices make a difference. Here are some golden tips to help control and prevent acne:

- When *thoroughly* washing your hair in the shower, keep your head held back and do not allow the water with product and oils to get on your face.
- Wash your body *after* you finish washing your hair to remove residue of hair product from your body.
- If you wash your hair in the sink, *do not* let product get on your face, which is why showers are the best place to wash your hair because you have more control.
- Style your hair before you apply your makeup.
- Wash your hands *thoroughly* to remove all oily, sticky hair products before you touch your skin.
- Cover your face with a towel before spraying hair spray.
- Do not touch your hair and then your face

as you will transfer hair products to your skin.

- Try to keep your hair away from your face to not allow hair product to touch your face at all.
- At bedtime, cover your hair with a scarf then follow with a bonnet on top.
- Trade out your pillowcase weekly. No dirty pillowcases.
- Exercise without wearing foundation and use a headband to keep sweat from running down your face.
- Always wash your face immediately after exercising.

Haircare Products and Ingredients That Cause Acne

One of the biggest acne culprits I see with my clients is hair products. We love our hair and love to add versatility by using products that contain oils. Unfortunately, this can cause mild to major acne breakouts. Think about it this way: when grease builds up on your pots and pans, it can be almost impossible to degrease them because oil is tough to remove. Keep that in mind when washing your hair and if you struggle with acne avoid using hair products that contain oils.

This is when the detective in you—you know that girl!—needs to put on the hat and trench coat, grab your handy magnifying glass, and get to investigating! Many products developed specifically for African American hair are saturated with oils, butters, and gels that stimulates acne. Some of the products may be ideal for the hair but terrible for the skin. The goal is to find balance and achieve both—great hair and great skin. Do not fret! It's possible; with your patience, newfound snootiness, and willingness to learn, you will achieve both. Here's how to start:

- Avoid products that add oil to your skin or hair.
- Look at the ingredient labels closely (*very important*).
- Have a magnifying glass handy when shopping for products as the words tend to be very tiny on products or search products online so you can zoom in.

Please do not let the following list freak you out. Do your best to avoid as many as you can. The oils and butters are top priority to avoid, and the rule of thumb for any product is the first ingredients on a label have the higher concentrations, and the ones at the end contain the least.[1] If it says "oil-free," it may still contain ingredients that cause breakouts so be sure to avoid:

- Silicone
- Sodium lauryl sulfate and ammonium lauryl sulfate
- PVP, CVP, and copolymer ingredients
- Petrolatum
- Apricot oil
- Coconut oil
- Peach kernel oil
- Palm oil
- Hemp seed oil
- Sweet almond oil
- Grape seed oil
- Rosehip oil
- Cocoa butter
- Shea butter
- Corn oil
- Cottonseed oil
- Meadow foam seed oil
- Soybean oil
- Wheat germ oil
- Olive oil
- Caprylic/capric triglyceride sorbitan oleate
- Botanicals
- Algae extract
- Carageenan

- Red algae
- Isopropyl myristate
- Isopropyl palmitate
- Isoparaffin C13-14
- Isopropyl linoleate
- Isopropyl lanolate
- Isopropyl isostearate
- Myristyl myristate

Acne and Zinc

You may or may not know that the largest organ of our body is our skin. Keeping this organ functioning properly and as healthy as possible requires we feed and care for it well! Zinc is one of the essential minerals that helps do just that. Not only does it supply benefits internally but also externally. This means not only will zinc make you feel better, but it will also help you look better. WOOOOO WHOOO!!! Who wants to sign up?

Due to its anti-inflammatory effects, zinc is ideal for acne and hyperpigmentation. The simple reasoning is because inflammation is almost always present where acne and discoloration exists. To reduce acne and discoloration, we must also reduce inflammation. So, zinc up!

Benefits of Collard Greens for Acne

Collard greens are unique because they are rich in the properties that support detoxification, are high in vitamins K and A, and they're also rich in soluble fiber and have strong antioxidant effects. By adding collard greens to your diet:

- You reduce disease-causing inflammation which includes acne.
- You help cure digestive conditions. (Keep in mind digestive issues can also worsen acne.)
- It detoxifies your body and boosts your cardiovascular health. (Detoxing the body of impurities helps to fight bacteria and control acne.)
- It helps the liver cleanse and detoxify fat.
- It boosts immune function.
- It fights cancer.
- It protects the body from environmental toxins.
- It helps the body absorb supplements and medications.

Collard greens contain a molecule called glutathione which is vital to our health. Researchers believe the levels of glutathione that are present in our cells serve as a predictor of how long we are going to live. Collard greens boost those levels and allow this molecule to do its magic. So eat up, beauties!

Maybe thinking about it now, you see ways that your habits and choices are breaking my "rules." You can keep on living with the consequences or try my tips and see how your skin clears. You're welcome in advance!

How to Know if You Have the Perfect Esthetician

Finding an esthetician that is a fit for you can be difficult, and when you do find one, you feel like you hit the lottery. Not all estheticians are the same, so these tips may be useful for you to have the best fit.

1. Your skincare treatments are customized to your specific skin needs and concerns during each visit.
2. At every visit, your esthetician discusses the health of your skin, which should include your improvements and/or things that still need to be worked on and addressed.
3. Your esthetician should be consistently educating you about your skin as well as the products you are using or should be using.
4. If you are prone to congestion and clogged pores, your esthetician should be giving you thorough extractions. I have never heard of

painless extractions that were thorough (so expect them to hurt). After each facial treatment, your pores should look and feel clean.

5. There is a myth that has been floating around for years that says after a facial your skin "should" break out. This is completely false. In fact, it is quite the opposite. Your skin should clear up after a facial. Facials are purging so only what was on its way out should show up after your facial. This shouldn't be a consistent occurrence if your esthetician is working with you to control your acne.

6. You should feel 100 percent supported with your skin. Your esthetician should feel like your accountability coach, your drill sergeant, your cheerleader, and your confidant. You should feel comfortable to discuss anything without feeling judged or ridiculed.

7. Lastly, you should feel you are in a safe, clean, and sterile environment while having your facial treatments.

Do not ever stop dreaming. It is a major ingredient to becoming who you were put here to be—Maisha

There are no miracles in skin care, only implementation, consistency, discipline, and a great esthetician. −Maisha

4

TWEENS AND TEENS

A positive attitude and a smile are two secrets to healthy skin. –Maisha

Cheer up Because We Are about to Clear Up

Hello, Tween and Teen!

I'd like to speak to you, and, with your permission, I'd like your parent, family members, and friends to listen in as well. Clearing you up and keeping you clear is truly a collective effort, so I'd like everyone you love and who loves you to be in on this. They need to know how best to support you. You matter! And your precious skin deserves all the attention you commit to giving it. Accept all the help from your loved ones that you can get! Can we make an agreement right now that your skin *can* be clear, *will* be clear, and these suggestions will help you achieve this? Great! Thanks!

Tweens

You are between the ages of nine and twelve and no longer a little child but not quite a teenager. You're likely excited for thirteen. It's coming, don't worry. In the meantime, let's learn about your skin.

Typically, playing sports, gaming with friends, sweating, face touching, dirty hands, not changing linen and face towels frequently, various hair products, and junk food affect your skin adversely. You might notice acne, the most common skin disorder that affects tweens and teens.

Acne is the occurrence of inflamed or infected oil glands. Oil and dead skin clog the pores and produces acne. The most common types of acne symptoms are:

- Whiteheads: These are pimples that stay under the surface of the skin.
- Blackheads: These are small specs of oil (sebum) clogging the pores, which the air oxidizes and turns the tip black just as when

an apple is cut and the white flesh turns brown from oxidation.

- Papules: These are small, flesh-colored bumps that can be tender.
- Pustules: These pimples are tender, and based on complexion, they can be red at the bottom and have pus on top.
- Nodules: These are large, painful, solid pimples that are deep in the skin.
- Cysts: These deep, painful, pus-filled pimples can cause scars.

Acne can be caused by hormonal changes, heredity, the start and stop of medications including birth control, diet, makeup, and the use of products that clog pores. Triggers can vary from one person to the next.

It is important during your tween and teen years to start practicing habits that encourage healthy skin. So when you are out and about with friends or playing sports, try not to touch your face with your hands or let anything come into contact with your face. If you sweat, use a cloth to wipe up. Try to minimize junk food and drink lots of water.

What is Going on with My Face?

You may notice small fine bumps or maybe even larger pimples we call papules and pustules on your skin. The above-mentioned activities will encourage this type of acne. You may also notice dryness and flaky, whitish, caked-up texture which appears as if the skin needs exfoliation (which means removing dead skin cells). You are correct that occasional exfoliation will be beneficial, but it's best not to use anything too harsh.

This is a perfect time for you to get started on a basic, simple, skincare system so you will see and feel a difference in your skin. You don't have to invest in things that are terribly expensive, but it's definitely time for you to move past using any random soap or lotion on the face.

If you choose not to take my suggestions right now, it's okay. It's your choice, and you get to make the decision. It's your skin. But let me ask you this: Is your skin important to you? Do you want clear skin? When you look in the mirror, what do you want to see? When you see yourself in a picture, what do you want to see? Is clear skin on your list? Well, if it is, I am going to teach you how you can do this simply.

At your age, breakouts are starting to happen, and it can seem really hard to figure out why. That's what I'm here for. I will help make it easy for you.

My Acne Story

I remember what it was like at your age to be
breaking out. My breakouts started in about the fifth
or sixth grade. It was a subtle beginning and progres-
sively got worse. I remember being the only one in
school or in my family with bad acne. Now, I will say, I
am absolutely sure I wasn't the only one with acne,
but I only focused on the kids with clear and perfect
skin, and I couldn't understand why my skin was so
blemished. There was a moment I hoped no one
noticed, but that wasn't the case. At every turn,
someone would point out the bump on my nose, forehead, or wherever else one would land. Then one
bump turned into a family of bumps taking residence
on my once clear, pretty face. It was very frustrating.
Yet, every day I chose to hold my head up as though it
didn't matter. It did matter to me, because I could
never look in the mirror without feeling disappointed
about the changes that were taking place right before
my eyes. The bumps turned into scars. I hated the
white pus that would come. They hurt like heck much
of the time. The pebbly rough texture when I
touched my face felt like a face I didn't know. I took
myself to various stores to try to find products that
claimed to help with acne, to no avail. My family
would tease and make light of my facial embarrass-
ment. I certainly didn't let them know how badly it
bothered me. But I cried when I was alone and prayed

for a solution to clear me up. My uncle William would often say, "Mai, your skin is clearing up, sweetheart."

I held on to his every skin compliment, hoping it was true.

I'm not sure where my grandfather got the idea, but one day he told me to get ready because he was taking me to the skin doctor (dermatologist). I got ready and off we went. I was so excited. This would be the first of many, many sessions and series of visits, treatments, and topical medications. After months of this and months of overusing the various topical medications the doctor prescribed, I had skin that was burning, irritated, and even more scarred. It wasn't working. I went back to taking matters into my own hands, back to the drug stores and buying any product I thought might help. Does any of this sound familiar?

What I learned later is that getting to the cause of what is breaking you out is far more important than what you use on your skin. Don't get me wrong, though. The products you need for your acne are important, but getting to the root of what is causing breakouts is far more crucial. It is what will control and stop them entirely. And that's our ultimate goal, right?

Teens

You are between the ages of thirteen and nineteen.
You are no longer a little child and likely have a bit
more freedom, but you're getting reminded you
haven't crossed that adult threshold yet. Oh, but it's
right around the corner! Be patient and let's take
care of your skin in the meantime.

Often around your age, interest in boys and girls
becomes a focus and how you present yourself to
the world does as well. So begins the makeup,
greasy/oily/buttery hair products, and the use of
body oil, lotions, perfumes/colognes. Not to
mention consuming junk food, which all can affect
the skin adversely.

It's Not Forever Even if It Feels Like It

I want you to know that this stage in your life is
temporary although it may feel like it will last
forever. I remember it like it was yesterday when I
was breaking out like crazy. I also remember some
adults telling me that because they experienced acne
as a child, they knew exactly how I felt. I was frustrated by those comments because they had no idea
how I felt inside. If you are feeling that way, I apolo-
gize. You are correct. I am not you, so I have no idea
exactly how you feel. So, if you'd like, email me and

tell me: info@skinbymaisha.com. Then, let's get you cleared up.

I may not know *exactly* how you feel, but I want you to know that I do have some idea based on experiencing tween and teen acne myself. I know it's frustrating, inconvenient, at times embarrassing, and sometimes it hurts. I mentioned getting to the root of the problem, so let's talk about that. Avoiding certain diet and lifestyle choices will help clear you up fast. You may not like the things I suggest you avoid, but if you do, you will clear up. Later in this chapter, I will list all the things I know to avoid. Follow that list to the letter, and watch your skin clear up.

The Agreement That Leads to Clear Skin

Let's agree about something. Your face is precious and everyone who loves you wants to give you a hand. It's just the way it is. They love you and want the best for you. Although you may be showing no interest in clearing up, or maybe you are, they want to help you show up as your best. I know when you hear some of them make comments like,

"She/He has acne like so and so."

Or, "I never had acne like that."

Or, "I don't know who he/she inherited that acne from. It looks so bad."

Those things are hard to hear. But here is a simple suggestion. When your loved ones make comments that you don't like, gently say, "That doesn't make me feel good, and I don't like when you say things like that."

Be open to expressing how you feel. Be sure to be kind when you speak, and you should receive kindness back. They are not saying these things to hurt you; they just don't know it bothers you. So, I need you to speak up. Deal? Now, let's speak up and clear up.

For Parents and Guardians (*and* Tweens and Teens)

Not every tween or teen experiences skin issues; however, it is still important to start them at this age caring for their skin in a very simple way. The sooner you start your young person, the more likely they will keep up great skin care habits for years to come, hence preserving the appearance and health of their skin. We were all this age once, and you either experienced some skin shifts during this time in life or knew a child that did, so you can sympathize with where your young person is. If you have forgotten what adolescent skin trouble is like, I hope reading this will be a gentle reminder for you.

Today with social media, there is a lot of peer pressure around pictures. At this age, self-image means a lot to our tweens and teens. Taking an interest in their skin is definitely a plus and helps with fostering their self-esteem during this crucial time. Building these young souls up is our duty and skin care is a major part of that, in my opinion. Their skin care does not have to be extensive but making it intentional is worth it to their future. Being sensitive about the blemishes they are experiencing is crucial. They may act as though they do not care, but generally, deep down, they do.

Making time to care for your skin together can be a fun thing to do, and it lets you share quality time. This helps to show the importance of self-care and that you care. It is important not to press the issue if your tween or teen is resistant. This is a good time to find an esthetician you are comfortable with and allow him or her to help warm your tween or teen up to the idea of caring for their skin.

Client Success Story: Faith C.

Faith was fourteen when she first began coming to me for treatments. For the few years I have been working with her, she has struggled not just with various types of acne and acne scarring, but also with blackheads, papules, pustules, nodules, and cysts. Faith is an athlete, but dolling up is just as important to her as her sports. She unfortunately loves all the wrong hair products, hair extensions, lip glosses, and body oils in addition to the foods and beverages that contribute to her breakouts. I was able to get her mom on board, so she has the entire family involved now. They try their best to keep all dairy, caffeine, and fabric softeners out of the house. Prior, it was a struggle for Faith because certain foods, her fashion, and form of expression, which are her various hair styles and lip glosses, were hard for her to change or give up. She has had her ebbs and flows of clearing up only to break out again because sometimes she returned back to old, bad habits. I once added another layer of accountability to her skin care, which was to write down everything she ate and drank daily and report it to me. We also did check-ins during the week, and her family made sure to keep all Faith's acne culprits out the house. We continued with maintenance facial treatments to include extractions and have advanced to chemical peels and HydraFacial treatments since she has gotten a better handle on avoiding her acne culprits. It has taken hard work and dedication, and I am happy to report Faith is seventeen now and practically clear! It took us three years, but she did it. I am so proud of her.

Client Success Story: Samuel J.

Samuel J., fifteen, came to me with acne, with many blackheads over most of his face as well as his inner ears and earlobes. After assessing his skin, my conclusion was his barbershop visits were probably the culprit. I advised him to stop letting the barber brush his face with the dusting brush he likely was using on every client without washing. I told him if he was spraying the duster brush, it might be the spray itself that could be causing the acne. I advised him not to let the barber spray his hair with the sheen either as I believe the spray was also contributing to the problem. As for the ear lobes, I asked if he was wearing headphones, and my suspicion was correct, he was. Of course, I recommended he find an alternative way to listen to his music. I began maintenance facial treatments, he made the changes I recommended, and he cleared up. Whew whooo!

Tips for Tweens and Teens

- Keep your hands clean and try not to touch your face.
- When sweating, use your shirt, top, towel, or tissue paper to wipe sweat.

- Wash your bed sheets once a week.
- Switch out your towel and face cloth to a fresh clean one once a week.
- Avoid greasy hair products and gels.
- Less is best in the hair.
- Diet is key. Minimizing is also key. To avoid the following suggestions entirely is not a reasonable expectation for most teens so simply minimize salty, sugary, and fried foods. Aim for a reasonably healthy, balanced diet.

Tips for Reducing Acne

- Do not pick at your skin. Picking at pimples can cause spreading of the acne, dark spots, and/or scarring.
- Cleanse skin with cool water, never hot.
- Change pillowcases weekly.
- Wrap hair at night.
- Avoid greases and oil in hair.
- Don't let your cell phone touch your face.

5

SKIN CARE IN YOUR TWENTIES

You are your number one priority and so is your skin.
–Maisha

How to Look and Be Your Best for Years to Come

You will never be this age again. Once you pass your twenties, what's done is done. This is not to discourage you; this is to encourage you. Make the most of each and every moment you have. Especially when it comes to your skin.

Every older person wishes they still had that youthful, tight skin they had in their twenties. Trust me. There is a funny quote that says, "Youth is wasted on the young." It means young people have so much opportunity and do not take advantage of it; rather, they take it for granted. Meanwhile, an older person will say, "Give me that young skin again! I'd take care of it so much better now that I know."

Defy that logic by taking control of your skin's future today. What you do today will make a difference five, ten, fifteen years from now and beyond. Now stretch yourself. What could you do to make a difference not just for your skin but for your entire life, which will affect your future five, ten, fifteen years from now?

Going within and working hard today to become your future self requires intentional work. You might feel like you have all the time in the world, or maybe you feel time is moving so fast, and you don't have much time at all. There is a saying that goes, "Live like there is no tomorrow, but live like you'll live forever." Really, that means find balance. Live and enjoy life, but pay attention to your future self at the same time. Don't keep putting *you* off. You are just as important as whatever is keeping you busy, preoccupied, or distracted from working on you. And truthfully, the time investment I'm recommending you make in yourself are simple practices that if you start today, will allow you to soar personally and professionally—before you know it.

For You...

Here are some ways to work on *you*. First, write down your goals and when you'd like to achieve them. Next, decide the steps you will take. Next, check into what resources or people would be ideal in helping you achieve those goals—who or what could hold you accountable to these steps. Are you surrounding yourself with positive, loving, and kind people that celebrate you? Are you celebrating yourself? Are you speaking kindly and lovingly to yourself? What are your habits? Our habits create our future. I know this is true. Create great habits today, and your future will be a reflection of that. This is related to your skin but also every piece of you as well.

Habits That Encourage Your Greatness

In my twenties, I did a lot of procrastinating. I allowed myself to believe I didn't have enough time, but the truth is I really didn't feel I was worthy. So I thought, "Why bother?" I felt that way about so many things I wanted to do. Truthfully, I struggled with not even feeling I was capable of doing many of the things I really wanted to do. A lot of self-doubt. It took me years to realize and learn there is absolutely nothing I can't do, and that applies to you as well. There is absolutely nothing you can't do. The question is are you willing to do the work? Are you willing to invest the time? Perhaps you may want to answer "yes," but the true answer is "no." Or perhaps these questions scare you, and you don't know how to answer them. This is a sure indication that it would be beneficial to work on *you*. By working diligently on you, you will uncover your superpowers. When you make *you* your focus, whatever you wish to achieve will be yours.

I spent a lot of time working on relationships with other people when I should have focused on the relationship with myself, which is why I encourage you to focus on you. That is not to say people aren't important. However, you cannot show up as your best for others if you aren't showing up as your best for you. That means spending time getting to know you, getting to learn your strengths, finding the things that excite you (or don't.) Map out your future, even if it changes from time to time. Read, study things that interest you, make sure you pay attention to your health and fitness even if it's just walking. These are the things, if I could go back in time, I would have done more of. Not to say I didn't do any of these things because I did. It was actually my saving grace, even though I was up and down, inconsistent. Greatness comes with consistent intentional application. And by greatness, I mean becoming who you were put here to be. Living your best life and looking your best self. The sooner you start, the easier it is in the long run. Start where you are because it's *never* too late! Do not just take my word for it either. Anyone that has accomplished greatness will tell you the same thing: create these habits now.

Skin Care Time

Another habit I'd like you to pay attention to is your skin care, because it certainly makes a difference in how you look and feel.

Your twenties are a time when you accept that you are an adult, and it's time to really act like one. This is true for skin care too. Commonly, you head to the various stores to shuffle through the hundreds of cosmetics available to you instead of seeking professional advice. Trying to do it yourself can cause a lot of frustration for you, your skin, and your pocketbook.

You want your skin to look its best, and in your twenties, the reasons make sense. Weddings arise, be it your own or your friends'. There are parties, work events, vacations, job interviews, and more. You may not have any skin concerns right now but wish to learn how to keep amazing skin for life. Maybe you are fed up with acne or other skin concerns you have been battling for years. You may be one of the rare ones who has never struggled with skin issues until now, and you are confused as to why they are showing up. Either way, you demand a solution to rid your skin of these annoyances for good and maintain healthy skin for life. No one wants to be in their sixties with acne, and I've seen it often. If you do not learn and understand how to control acne at an early age, you run the risk of suffering with acne and hyperpigmentation/discoloration for years to come. Learning proper skin care in your twenties will gain you amazing skin for life! You will get older, it is inevitable, but you do not have to ever look it! That is what caring for your skin ensures you.

It is important to shop for makeup brands that are non-comedogenic (will not clog the pores), which will eventually cause acne. For your everyday makeup, you want to select light, breathable makeup that is geared towards skin care as well as coverage.

Client Success Story: Asha M.

One of my clients, Asha M., twenty-nine, came in with severely scarred skin and acne. She had been struggling with acne and picking, and severe scarring was the result. She had been seeing another esthetician who was a good friend of her family. She had used many skincare products but wasn't getting any results. Someone recommended she visit me, and she did. I started Asha with a consultation and

learned she was using haircare products that were
full of oil, sheens, butters, and gels that were stimulating her breakouts. She was also eating foods that
contained dairy and caffeine, which were also
contributing to her breakouts and irritation. Her
detergents contained softeners and fragrances,
which were also exacerbating the problem. I advised
Asha I would not give her a facial that day because I
wanted her to start with my homecare system of
skincare products to prepare her skin for my professional treatments. I also wanted her to begin using
the advice I gave her. If you don't follow my advice
of things to avoid, nothing you use on your skin will
help you gain the results you are looking for. You
must address the root of the problem rather than
just cover it up or treat it with topicals (serums,
medications, or any leave-on products).

Even after several visits with Asha, we found under-
lining culprits that were breaking her out. One of
the last culprits we discovered were her two lovely
cats that would sleep with her and on her pillows.
Once we stopped that, she cleared completely. Asha
continued to come in for treatments which included
extractions, chemical peels, microdermabrasion, and
oxygen treatments to name a few. I also gave her a
complete homecare skin system to include lactic
acid, L-ascorbic acid, lightening and brightening
serums, salicylic acid, retinol, niacinamide, and

other active ingredients that helped her clear up. Asha always had a very upbeat and positive attitude around clearing up. Every step of the way she was cooperative and willing to do whatever it took, which helped her gain her results so fast.

Client Success story: Aliyah B.

Aliyah, now twenty-nine, began coming to me for facials when she was twenty-two years old. She was a student at Cal State Hayward and originally contacted me to speak on a panel for a health and wellness event she was organizing at her school. She had no idea that though I had been given many opportunities to speak at events, I had always declined because of my fear of public speaking. However, around the time she reached out to me, I had been getting a calling from within to speak publicly. I told God that if anyone asked me, I would say yes. Out of nowhere this little angel called to invite me to speak.

Directly after our call she scheduled a facial appointment and began her skin care journey with me. She helped me push past my fear of public speaking a bit more, and I helped her clear up her skin. Aliyah had advanced acne, acne scarring and pitting, asphyxiated acne, blackheads, a lot of congestion in her pores. She also had allergies that were causing irritation, dryness, and discoloration.

We certainly had our work cut out for us, but Aliyah was up for the challenge and so was I.

Because she was a college student at the time, budget was certainly a factor, so we started with basic facials and home care products. We did several sessions of extractions to clear her pores of the congestion which helped her skin tremendously. It would take quite some time for Aliyah to buckle down and remove all the culprits that were causing her breakouts. They included dairy, caffeine, hair oils, various hair products and styles, body oils and heavy lotions, detergents with fragrance and fabric softeners. Getting her to eliminate many of the hair products and hair extensions was also something we needed to tackle. Over the years she would do well and then go back to her bad habits. She finally buckled down and invested in the skin care products I recommended for her, which included exfoliating, brightening and antioxidant serums. We also stepped up her facial treatments from basic facials to our more advanced treatments which included chemical peels. I am so proud and happy to report that at twenty-nine years old Aliyah is all cleared up! She cut all the culprits out of her diet and lifestyle and found ways to style her hair that helps her skin stay clear. Her diet is impeccable! In fact, she is a nutrition counselor now, and she clearly applies it to her own life, because she glows from the inside out.

Aliyah has always glowed, I must say. Her personality has always been bubbly and full of life. Now her beautiful skin allows her to shine even brighter. Aliyah for the skin care win!

My Recommendations for Twenties Skin

This is the time in life to get serious about skincare products. The steps to your system should include:

- A double cleanse if you are wearing makeup.
- Corrective serums to fight free radical damage and discoloration.
- Eye cream to preserve, hydrate, and protect that under-eye area and the lids.
- Moisturizer to keep skin hydrated and preserved.
- Sunscreen every day, no exception. The sun damages skin no matter our race and causes us to age fast!

You will thank me when you are in your sixties, so I'll say "you're welcome" in advance.

Always be open to learning more. You will only improve if you do. —Maisha

6

THIRTIES SKIN CARE

Let love lift you. –*Maisha*

Setting the Stage for Your Next Performance

The thirties are a time when you realize and accept that you are not a girl anymore. You typically notice a gravity shift in your skin, and more often than not, you freak the heck out! Yikes!! You begin to question what you see in the mirror. You might have some self-doubt. Do I still look young? Am I aging gracefully? Do I look my age?

Maybe you are questioning where you are in life, personally and professionally, and you're thinking about where you want to go. You might be asking questions like, have I made good use of my time, have I wasted my time, am I on track with my goals, have I set high enough goals, am I getting too old to do this or that?

At this age, a major light comes on and a voice says, "Let's get it together." This is an amazing time in your life, and it is preparing you for greater days ahead, so do not let that voice scare you. Rather, let it fuel you to answer those questions and do something about them. The key is to be gentle and patient with yourself. Know that wherever you are in your journey, you have what it takes to accomplish and achieve all your dreams, goals, and desires.

When I hit thirty, that bright light switched on for me. I felt good, but I wanted some changes to happen. I was a single mother and taking a pause on dating, getting to know me. A couple of years prior I had lost my friend, sister, and mentor. She was taken from this earth. It made the end of my twenties and early thirties a difficult patch. I enveloped myself in spirituality, and I reached as high as I could for God's hand. I desperately wanted to know what feeling closer to my Creator meant, looked like, and felt like. At that time, a scripture I remembered as a child in church came to me, "Create in me a clean heart and renew the right spirit within me." I would

silently recite that as often as I could. I can't say I
knew what that meant exactly, but what it felt to me
was, "Change me so that the things around me can
change."

I was busy trying to build my business, raise my
daughter, maintain healthy friendships, and it all felt
like such a struggle. I was sad, grieving, lost, feeling
alone and lonely, curious, and frankly scared.

A couple of years later, I got married and poured the
remainder of my thirties into my marriage, my business, and my daughter. I can't say I did enough work
on myself. There were far too many distractions that
I allowed to hold me back from doing the real work.
I gave some focus to myself here and there, but I
wasn't diligent or patient, nor did I continue implementing the things I knew I needed to be doing to
work on me. Perhaps, if I had, I would be in a
different place today. But no regrets, because then I
wouldn't have this advice today to offer encouragement for you now and ahead.

Treasure Your Thirties

The thirties can feel like your second chance at
your twenties. You're still incredibly young; your
twenties aren't that far away. You know you have
plenty of time to make up wherever you fell off.
Working out is still easy to start, eating healthy,

giving your skin dedicated attention, taking a class, reading books related to your interests, fostering relationships that serve you in a healthy and positive way—it all still feels possible. You still have a feeling of resiliency, energy; you've not been tainted by life's adversities, and if you have encountered them, you haven't been scorned and scarred. You're still hopeful about friends; you're still willing to risk and learn.

Things get better in your thirties. You may find yourself less afraid to initiate conversations and network with interesting people. If you shied away in your twenties, now you get a redo. We get to exercise our confidence a bit more and see that people generally want exactly what we want...to connect with great people just like us. Right now, it doesn't matter whether you are married or single, have many friends, few friends, or no friends. You are so incredibly important. Make time to invest in you, and work on you. Whatever your dream, goals, and aspirations are, set all doubts and fears aside for now, and just do whatever it takes to start the process of making them happen.

Get what you need. Where is your support? Who can be your support? What do you need to start making some of these things happen? What books can you read on the subject? Who can you hire to guide you and coach you? I am happy to be that coach for you. Listen, there is always a way. There is no such thing as "can't," only "won't." Let's go, thirty!

Thirties Skin

While on this journey through your thirties, it helps to face every step with healthy, glowing skin. What I am certain of is that you don't want to look exactly your age. Most of us want to look younger, and we recognize this fact in or around our thirties. This is what makes skin care such a special treat. It slows down the process of aging. The results have been proven. Skin care is not a multibillion-dollar business for nothing. This is definitely the time to invest in your skin and make it count. You have amazing years ahead of you, and you can commit now to looking your absolute best in each and every one of them.

Commit to Improving Your Skin

You may still be experiencing breakouts if you've not yet learned how to control them. Please take a look at the acne chapter for more advice. You may be dealing with discoloration and starting to notice the development of tiny, faint freckles. If you have not learned proper skin care, you run the risk of aging much faster. You may be fed up and demanding a solution for acne, acne scars, and dull-blah skin, and you want that fresh twenties face again. You may even be screaming, "Skin care to the rescue!"

Maybe all of these things apply or just a few, but either way, you are seeking to improve or maintain the health of your skin for life. You know you will age, but the goal is that you keep looking as young as possible for as long as possible! That is the reward for caring for your skin.

Your Skin Is a Celebrity if You Treat It Like One

There are tons of trends and many makeup brands on the market. It's fun to experiment, but be sure when selecting makeup to get trial sizes first. Test it out to make sure it doesn't break you out. It may even be too heavy or oily which over time can cause acne breakouts. Be sure that you are consistently using your homecare skincare regimen morning and night. Make this a habit and never stop. It's the one habit that pays off in the long run, and your skin will always be the topic of positive conversation. It feels good when people notice all the hard work you've put into your skin. They'll want to know what you do, what you use. Depending on your personality, you may share, or you may do as some of my clients and say that you do nothing; your grandmother has great skin, and you got it from her. Your choice. You absolutely don't have to share your secrets, but my point is your skin will be a celebrity if you treat it like one.

No matter what, please, make this decade count. Whatever you are doing right, as Grant Cardone, author of *The 10X Rule* says, "10X it!" You will be so thankful you did when you reach your forties. It sets the stage for that work, I promise.

Client Success Story: Gayle S.

My client, Gayle S., thirty-five, came to me with blemished skin, asphyxiated acne, and hyperpigmentation. She had been struggling with acne for many years, all through high school into her thirties. She was fed up and demanded a change. I was incredibly excited to work with her because for years I would see her, as we were a part of the same circle of friends. However, I never discussed her skin with her, skin is always my focus. I personally feel it is rude to discuss skin care unless I am asked. I am known to offer unsolicited advice with the exception of skin care. It is one of the areas in my life (and I have a few) I hold a sacred space for and pay so much respect to. However, I notice everything when it comes to a face. So, though she never knew, I desperately wanted to work with her.

When Gayle walked through my door for her first appointment, I was thrilled! I worked with her to change many bad habits she had formed over the years and had no idea they were bad or the very culprits causing her acne. The habits included using certain haircare and body products, perfume, and lip ointments. Of course, I had her begin a homecare regimen to combat acne and discoloration, as well as to hydrate and protect her skin.

We began a series of treatments consisting of various chemical peels, microdermabrasion, and oxygen treatments all to gain her the success she has today—clear and flawless skin. Her skin is truly the talk of the town. She is quite a beautiful girl, but her skin needs its own zip code! It's that stunning.

What I love about Gayle is that her inner beauty truly matches her flawless skin. Over the years, she has shared part of her story about her childhood, which was very difficult. She faced challenges that would have held many people back. But not Gayle. She allowed those challenges to fuel her forward to beat every odd.

I love to hear success stories, victory stories, as they touch my heart and quite honestly, inspire me. I am a believer that no matter the struggle, tragedy, or trauma, we were all born and built to make it. Not just to survive but thrive! I love to see examples of this truth, and Gayle is definitely one!

I know oftentimes it can feel and appear as if the odds are all stacked against you, but that is merely fear (false evidence appearing real) causing you to think and believe the worst which inevitably will hold you back and stop you from accomplishing what you are aiming for. Perseverance, a positive attitude, and faith in a higher source, which Gayle demonstrates in her life, are a few keys to thriving and reaching your goals. Gayle is now a registered nurse and on her way to becoming a nurse educator, which is her passion. I am so proud to have her as my client and friend.

Client Success Story: Kim U.

Kim U., thirty-nine, came to me with cystic acne and scarring. She was also an avid picker. I consulted with her about what she needed to change, and the picking was a major component. Unless we could control and eliminate the picking, the scaring would never go away. I would not allow her to go into her forties this way. Not on my watch! If she didn't stop the picking, it would be an uphill battle. Once we cleared old scars, she would create new scars, and this is what we call a vicious cycle. She was a habitual picker, so I knew I had to work with Kim to immediately control the breakouts, so she'd have nothing to pick. What I loved about Kim is she was always honest. If she picked, she would say she did. I have worked with so many clients over the years who weren't so forthcoming with what they were doing.

What many don't know is most experienced estheticians have a sixth sense. We know when you've been naughty, and we know when you've been nice to your skin. You might tell me, "I've been doing everything you said to do and don't do," or, "I don't eat anything but vegetables and drink water."

Oh, brother! I've heard it all, but as Oprah says, this is what I know for sure: if you do as I recommend and follow it to the letter, you *will* clear up. Honestly, I have had to tell some clients that I am not a fit for them because I know they won't change their bad habits. I do not wish to work with clients that say I am their esthetician if they refuse to follow my recommendations. Their skin does not represent my work.

Optimism Is Necessary to Get the Results You Desire

I am dedicated to helping my clients achieve their skin goals if they are willing to do the work. Most clients are willing, although occasionally I encounter some who challenge the process and are only interested in being negative, refusing to follow my recommendations, and not getting the results we intend to have. I have found the time I invest is not worth it in the long run. It usually ends up with both of us being incredibly disappointed, so I am sure to avoid this kind of outcome at all costs.

Back to Kim...she cleared up! I am so incredibly proud of her. As she pursues her entertainment career wearing makeup to only enhance her beauty rather than cover up her blemishes, I am so proud to say she trusted her skin in my hands and gained the results she was seeking.

Some Simple Tips for Skin Care in Your Thirties

- Don't forget to switch out linen and face towels weekly, and do not use fabric softeners as they stimulate acne and cause irritation on sensitive skin.
- Do not use hair products that contain oils, petroleum, hair sprays, or gels. Try to minimize hair product as much as you can.
- Use a scarf and bonnet to cover the hair every night making sure the hair isn't contacting the pillow which contacts your face.
- Don't sleep in makeup.

- Keep your diet as healthy and as clean as possible.

Your Skin Is a Reflection of Your Choices

Now is the time to step it up. If you've been lax about skin care, it's time to make a shift and get serious and active. The steps to your system should include:

- Cleansing morning and night. If you are wearing makeup, do a pre-cleanse with a gentle, creamy cleanser or do a double cleanse.
- Be sure you are using corrective serums to fight free radical damage and discoloration as well as serums that stimulate collagen and elastin production.
- Using an eye cream is essential. There are many on the market, so do your research for those with active and effective ingredients. They aren't cheap but neither are you when it comes to your skin.
- Be sure to use a moisturizer to keep skin hydrated.
- Have a "no exceptions" rule when it comes to sunscreen. Wear it every day, no exception. The sun is a number one factor

that causes the skin to age faster, no matter your race or complexion.

What You Do Today Will Determine What You See Tomorrow

If you follow these tips, I assure you that you will be looking to thank me years down the line. I remember in my early twenties a gentleman told me you can always tell a woman's age by her hands and eyes. He said always take care of them. He was an older gentleman, and I often think of him. I wish I could hug and thank him because I took his advice, and it worked. I always wear gloves when washing dishes, and I always wear an eye cream at least.

Always get professional advice for a system that is perfect and customized just for you. Remember you are worth it and so is your thirties skin. Care for it today, and tomorrow it will thank you.

How to Get Your Best Skin for Your Thirties and Beyond

How to get the best skin now and for the rest of your life requires commitment, dedication, and implementation. Are you willing to make this investment to get the skin you want? If so, here is the "how."

Drink Plenty of Water

I say it always, and I will say it again...water has amazing benefits and aids in keeping your skin plump, glowing, and clear. It will also help to keep your digestion regular, which helps rid the body of toxins. It is essential to stay hydrated, but it is not the answer to all your skin care woes. Water alone is not enough, but it is a great place to start.

Topical Magic

The application of your skin care is what drives it all home and creates the magic. These topicals are referred to as the ABCs and the BLTs of skin care.

A: Derived from vitamin A, retinol is one powerful *antioxidant* that aids cell turnover, slows down and reverses signs of aging, and controls acne and discoloration leaving skin radiant.

B: Stands for broad-spectrum SPF (sun protection factor). Using sunscreen to protect your skin from UVA/UVB rays is vital. Many sunscreens are not broad spectrum so check the label to be sure that yours is. Wear your SPF 365 days a year, no exception.

C: Vitamin C. The list goes on and on with benefits from this power antioxidant topical. It brightens, increases collagen production, fights acne-causing bacteria, reduces inflammation, promotes healing, is a sunscreen additive, and gives the skin a supple and beautiful glow.

Making sure you are diligent with your ABCs every day will ensure you healthy, glowing skin for life, and who on earth doesn't want that? Vitamin A, your broad-spectrum sunscreen, and topical vitamin C applied daily has been proven to slow down and even reverse signs of aging by protecting your skin against free radicals and stimulating collagen and elastin on a deep, cellular level. It will also promote firmer skin and reduce fine lines and wrinkles. So, don't just learn your ABCs, let's use them as well!

Brighteners, Lighteners, and Tighteners

A client, Tina, came in for her first visit with me. Her concern was her deep wrinkles and age spots. I agreed that her skin needed some special and intentional attention. She shared with me her age, and we realized our children had gone to high school together. Tina agreed that her skin was not a great representation of her age, and we worked together to turn that around. She added niacinamides, retinols, antioxidants, hyaluronic acids, and peptides to her skincare routine, and the next month I saw her, she had gained drastic improvement. Her skin was brighter, lighter, firmer, and she looked so refreshed. She already had a happy-go-lucky personality, but she shined energetically even more. Score! Maisha for the win! I love helping my clients gain these kinds of results, and you can have them too.

B stands for brighteners. Brightening topical treatments should be applied to keep the skin tone even. You can try vitamin C, azelaic acid, and kojic acid as well as a retinol.

L is for lighteners, which will inhibit hyperpigmentation and lighten discoloration. Good products include ingredients like vitamin C, retinol, arbutin, bearberry, and niacinamide to name a few.

T is for tighteners, which will increase collagen production, encourage firmer skin, and smooth out fine lines and wrinkles. Try products with ingredients like vitamin C, peptides, retinol, and hyaluronic acid.

There is something about great skin that makes you feel more empowered. –Maisha

7
_____

FORTIES SKIN CARE

Who sows courtesy reaps friendship; who plants kindness reaps love. –*Saint Basil*

You've Never Had a Friend so True

Soooooo, you're in your forties? Welcome! Likely, you understand skin care is necessary, and you are looking to reverse or slow down the process of aging. You know women who take really good care of their skin, and you may be one of them. You also know that taking care of your skin pays off, so you know at this stage in life it is important to pay special attention to it.

You may be fresh out of your thirties or deep into your forties or right in between. Either way, the forties are for sure skin care time. It is also "loving on you" time. You are learning about this "loving on you" thing. And, even if you were doing it all along, you might be realizing there is an entire other level that you must be on if you truly want to love yourself. You might feel a bit curious, and you're considering what steps you will take to do it. Sound anything like you or someone you know?

If you are not enjoying this time in your life, there is likely a specific reason why. The forties can be tough because things are really changing. Maybe you feel less in control of your life, like what you want is just out of reach, and you can never attain it. Maybe you feel all your efforts to be the woman you want to be are falling short.

Or you could be feeling very much in control. Maybe you feel like a unicorn because things are going so great that you doubt you deserve all this wonder. Maybe you are waiting for the bottom to fall out because things are just too good. Sometimes when we feel happy and powerful, we worry about what people will think, so we doubt ourselves or dim our light. Whatever you are feeling, remember, this moment is where you are supposed to be. It's all by design, trust me!

I've learned that the feeling of control always comes from within us. All we can truly control is our thoughts and actions—which is a lot, by the way. Start by remembering that what you feel is temporary. All emotions ebb and flow, and regardless of what you're feeling, it won't last forever. I've also learned that you can fix how you feel with your thoughts. Of course, it's almost impossible to control your thoughts all of the time, but trying to think positively no matter what is happening around you is a great skill to learn. It's definitely work and takes continuous practice, but it's worth the reward.

The Arrival of You

I've heard it said that if life is not scaring you, you are not living big enough. Are you living big enough? Are you doing the things you always wanted to do (deep down)? Being the person you truly always wanted to be? Where are you at with the goals you set out to accomplish in your twenties and thirties?

When I turned forty, I was in a marriage, but I felt so alone. I had, after many years of denial, accepted and finally made the decision in my heart and mind that my marriage wasn't going to work. I was convinced and pretty scared. I felt like I was in a tangled web, and I had no idea how to get out of it. My daughter was away in college, and I was faced with some real soul-searching. I read. I poured myself into my work and business. I started fostering better friendships, particularly the one with myself. Although it wouldn't be until the end of my forties that I truly got to know myself and fall in love with me. It was the first time I felt like my truest self. I found me. I was accepting of my flaws. I learned to be less critical of myself and more embracing of the person I had become.

When I was about forty-six, I made a no-compromise decision to "do me." I was fed up with just accepting anything that showed up in my life. I was fed up, frankly, with allowing someone else to guide me rather than my Higher Source and myself guiding me, which has always been my ultimate desire. I truly lifted my hands and said, "Guide me, God!" Two years later, my marriage ended, and I felt freer than I'd ever felt in my life. I realized I married the wrong person. But no regrets. Everything happens as it should. I learned so much. The biggest lesson I learned is that it is no one's responsibility to love you, believe in you, or to be fair to you. The responsibly is all your own!

Now at the end of my forties, I am going to miss the woman I was in that decade because she is the reason I became the woman I wanted to be. She was the best friend I've ever had in my life thus far. Throughout my forties, I wasn't feeling the love I thought I had signed up for: my daughter had her own boyfriend and life; my friends, though they loved me, weren't available 24/7, so I truly had to get to know this thing called "forties" attached to this chick named Maisha Pulliam. No matter how hard I tried to find distractions, nothing could distract myself from me. So boyyyee oh boyeee did I get to know her. I surely wish I'd believed in myself more, but today I could scream and shout in gratitude. I refused to give up on myself being an incredible mother, friend, and entrepreneur. And, of course, I refused to give up on my skin care!

The Surprises of Life

I have spent twenty-one years doing skin care and have built a practice full of amazing, loyal clients. As I was building my business, I never imagined there would come a day I would have clients on my waiting list wanting to receive my services. This still leaves me in awe. I remember days when I didn't have a single client, and I would cry under my facial bed because no one was on top of it. I would remember the John Updike quote, "Dreams come true! Without that possibility, nature would not incite us to have them."

For years, I prayed to be surrounded by amazing people, but I had no idea the people would come through skin care! Skin care has been a blessing and

a gift that hasn't ceased giving. That is what perseverance rewards you with—your wildest dreams. I
didn't give up, and I hope you don't either. During
the pandemic of 2020, I could not operate my business. I still heard that voice that said, "Don't give
up. I will take care of you."

I am here to tell you, whatever your dreams, goals,
or aspirations, don't you dare give up. I don't care
how hard, bleak, and hopeless things may seem; you
keep pushing forward. I say to you, Dreamer, dream,
and don't let that dream die, and you will see that
one manifest, along with many more. I know you
have more. When my business was closed, I was
able to work on a dream I had since I was a little
girl: writing this book. Yes, forty has been a gift to
me, and I love her so. She has been brutally honest
with me, but that is the best kind of friend we could
ever hope for.

The Changes Forties Bring for Your Skin

By now you likely have heard of antioxidants,
retinols, exfoliation, sunscreen, free radicals, and
vitamin C, which are all common terms. But do
you know what they mean or what they are for? In
your forties, cellular turnover has drastically
decreased since your twenties. That means subtle
fine lines, larger pores, the "11s" between the
eyebrows, those good ole lovely impression lines,

dull skin, lackluster skin, moles, and hyperpigmentation/uneven skin tone have started to sink in, and your skin isn't as radiant as it once was. Hormonal shifts begin to occur as well. It could be due to medications, changes with or discontinuing birth control, diet, or weight loss or gain. The production of elastin and collagen which once kept the skin firm, smooth, and toned begins to decrease as well. The skin becomes drier, and the skin doesn't retain its moisture as it once did. Transepidermal water loss is quite common during this stage in life, meaning the water in your skin evaporates quickly and easily, leaving the skin compromised and at risk of aging fast and being quite sensitive.

In your forties, you may still be experiencing breakouts if you've not yet learned how to control them. Refer to the chapters about acne as well as the chapters for tweens, teens, twenties and thirties. The same information on prevention and control apply to you. Learning proper skin care in your forties will gain you incredible skin for the rest of your life! No matter how old you get, making sure you don't look it is the goal. You will make that happen by caring for your skin always. This is the time in life to get serious about skincare products and having a thorough regimen to keep your skin hydrated and infused with as many nutrients as possible is essential. Load up on antioxidants that includes a retinol as well. And remember...sunscreen always!

Client Success Story: D.D.

My client, D.D., forty-nine, had been coming to me for facial treatments for at least seventeen years. Her skin had always been clear and flawless, no concerns other than a little dryness. She wanted to preserve the health of her skin for years to come. A few years ago, her skin shifted. I believed it was reacting adversely to dairy, caffeine, and fabric softener, to name a few. She went to see a dermatologist and was prescribed topical medication to alleviate the problem. As I mentioned earlier, I believe in always getting to the root of the problem rather than simply just treating it. That is the detective in me, but I also believe it is the best way to serve our skin. At all costs, I try to avoid medications as they typically have side effects when used long-term.

I tried to convince D.D. that she had reached a time in her life that her already sensitive skin is more sensitive now. Her allergies had heightened. My personal theory is that when we age, our immune system weakens, and the allergies become more aggressive, making us sensitive to things we once were not sensitive to. My suggestion to her was to avoid dairy, dairy replacements, caffeine, and detergents with dyes, fragrances, and softeners. She has had a challenge eliminating these things, and her skin is suffering because of it. Her skin is extremely dry, aged looking, dehydrated, and lackluster.

Client Success Story: Felecia S.

Felecia S. started coming to me for facial treatments when she was thirty-six and still comes to this day. When I began working with her skin, she had advanced melasma, acne, acne scaring, and sensitive skin. We cleared her skin completely, and for years, we maintained her beautiful, flawless, glowing skin. Toward the end of her forties, her skin shifted, and she became hypersensitive, experiencing rashes, severe dryness around her eyes, and dermatitis. As I did with D.D., I recommended she avoid all the same allergy culprits. Unlike my client D.D., Felicia avoided everything I suggested, and her skin normalized. She is extremely strict about her diet and lifestyle to maintain her healthy skin. Her skin glows and looks like baby fresh skin. No one would ever guess she is fifty-five years old. In fact, she looks just like the thirty-six-year-old I met nineteen years ago thanks to skin care and healthy habits.

Tips for Forties

- Focus on exfoliation.

- Remember eye cream and sunscreen are key.
- Use brightening serums and antioxidant serums to fight free radical damage that causes skin to age and discolor.
- Moisturize to keep skin hydrated and preserved, and use a sunscreen every day, no exception. The sun damages skin, no matter your race, and causes us to age fast!

Love Yourself Forward

No matter how amazing life is for you right now or how scary it might feel, pay attention to self-care, including your skin care, and know...life gets better and better! Wherever you are is where you are supposed to be. Trust the process and *love* on you all the way through.

Skincare Tips for You in Your Forties

1. Don't squeeze pimples. It does not make them go away faster. It actually creates a deeper scar and discoloration which will linger around for longer than if it were just left alone.
2. Cocktail all your skincare serums together to save time. The old way of applying more than one skincare serum was to layer on one

by one. This is not necessary. You can still obtain all the benefits of each serum and save time by mixing all your serums together on your fingertips and applying all over your skin.

3. Treat your neck and décolleté as part of your face. Your décolleté is susceptible to the same signs of skin damage as your face, so take the residual skincare product on your hands after applying to the face and apply to the neck and upper chest area.

4. Keep your eye cream and moisturizer in the fridge. This helps to reduce puffiness under the eye and all over the face.

5. Massage your face while applying your skincare products. Take your time while applying your products. When you gently massage your products into your face, you're able to boost circulation and create a fresher looking complexion.

The Benefits of Proper Exfoliation

As we age, our skin cells become sluggish and do not shed as they should. They stick around, which is not a good thing. The shedding of dead cells that used to take a month to turnover now remain glued in place for two to three months longer. This prolonged adhesion can cause a buildup of scaly, flaky skin and a compromised barrier which is our most outer skin layer. This leads to water loss within our skin barrier. If bacteria is present, breakouts will also be present, even with mature skin. Broken and compromised blood vessels exacerbate the issue because the body's self-cleansing function breaks down and oxygen cannot feed the skin cells.

Exfoliation speeds up cell turnover, dissolves congestion clogged within pores, stimulates the skin to produce collagen, and, if performed on a regular basis, gradually helps to fade hyperpigmentation, plump, and hydrate to reveal softer, smoother skin. Removal of dead skin layers allows for a deeper infusion of your products that follow, which should be your toner, serums, and moisturizer.

Two common forms of exfoliation are mechanical and chemical. Mechanical exfoliation can be done with hard substances such as exfoliating beads, loofahs, and devices like microdermabrasion. Chemical exfoliation is done with topical acids or enzymes such as lactic acid, glycolic, salicylic, bromelain, and papain.

In this life, I have learned you win some and you lose some, but, in due time, you gain everything you need! Trust the process. –Maisha

8

FIFTIES SKIN CARE

Let your light within shine. You will draw all you desire right to you —Maisha

Refusing to Settle for Anything Less Than the Best

This marks the decade of the happiness, wisdom, love, and balance that you have waited for your entire life. You didn't think fifty would come this soon, but it's here, and if you are like me, you want to embrace it and pray your next fifty years is even better than your first! If you've put in the time, work, and effort, it'll surely be the case. You know there is more intentional work to be done on you; however, I hope you feel a sense of accomplishment that you've made it this far. Yes, some days you have your doubts, fear may kick in, but you have learned to re-center yourself and remind yourself that you can do anything and be anything. Whatever doesn't make sense can be figured out. You are learning to stress less and trust that everything works out as it should. We are guided, even when it doesn't feel like it. Does that sound about right?

Because this for many is a period of reflection, acceptance, and peace, I believe this is the perfect time to clear your busy schedules periodically and go away to places with beautiful sceneries that allow you some quiet and relaxation. This is a time in life to reward yourself the most. Speak to yourself about how deserving and important you are. How capable and awesome you are. We all need ego boosters from time to time, but you've also learned by now if no one is encouraging you, as one of my favorite songs in church we sang as a child would say, "Encourage yourself."

I encourage you to reflect on all the things you have wanted to do and for whatever reason have not. If there is still an internal burning desire, even if the flames are just flickering and the flame isn't as big anymore, decide today to put some action plans in motion to get started on those things. Why not? If you are feeling like you imagined yourself being someone else at this age, or maybe even doing more, I ask you: What's stopping you right now from becoming who you wish to be and doing what you wish to do? Look at some of the fifty-year-olds that you admire and study what it is about them that is most impressive to you and start implementing what works and aligns with you and for you. This is a sure-fire way to your road to success. We must push forward and give this decade all we have. I truly believe this is the time, more than any, to refuse to settle for anything less than the absolute best.

Fifties Skin

This is a time to do the things that make you feel and look good. It is also the time of collagen loss when you might begin noticing saggy skin, impression lines, and less plumpness in your skin. This new adventurous journey called perimenopause, and for some menopause, affects nearly every woman in her fifties and tells her estrogen levels to go down, down, down. This decline causes collagen production to decrease significantly and the skin to become drier. It is important at this stage to hydrate within, but perhaps, it may be time to change your moisturizer if you are feeling especially dry. Also, peptides and hyaluronic acid serums will aid the skin in plumping up and bring you hydrating benefits. At fifty, you want to be using as many antioxidants as possible (eating them as well) as antioxidants help to fight free radicals which attack and damage the skin cells causing us to age faster. Some examples of antioxidants are vitamin C (L-ascorbic acid), vitamin A (retinol), and vitamin B (niacinamide). Getting monthly facials will also be a huge benefit to help keep your skin healthy and youthful. Facial treatments are designed to increase cell turnover, stimulating collagen and elastin, helping to keep the skin firm. Also, to keep the skin's texture smooth, bright, and glowing.

Client Success Story: Yvonne B.

Yvonne B. started coming to me for facial services when she was thirty-six years old. She is now fifty, and I must say, she still looks as youthful as the day I first met her! Skin care is certainly a winning game. She had been going to someone else for facials and decided she would try me, and almost fifteen years later, she is still my client.

When Yvonne and I first began working together, she struggled with extremely dry skin, acne, acne scaring, and discoloration. I have worked with her for years to eliminate the culprits. This has been a challenge. Many times, as estheticians, we can give a client all the reasons and possibilities why they are breaking out or experiencing extreme cases of dry skin, but if the client does not make those changes, unfortunately, they will likely not experience improvement with their skin, and the vicious cycle of breakouts and scaring will continue.

Clients depend on their skincare therapist to fix the annoyance of skin issues, and I have always been up for the job! But I am sure my clients will agree that my conversations and lectures can get a little repetitious. I do my best to urge my clients to follow my instructions to avoid certain culprits, as difficult as it may be. I tell them to avoid things like certain hair and lip products, but when a client is convinced that these are the only products that work, it's incredibly hard for them to give them up. But with continued sessions of my persistent advice, most clients give in, avoid the culprits, and clear up.

Yvonne loves her hair shiny and healthy and has used many products that work for her hair but cause acne. Her lips get really dry so avoiding lip balms with petroleum, which causes acne, was hard for Yvonne to do. She loves to smell good so fabric softeners were another thing she couldn't let go of. In addition, her husband and son both refused to give up the softeners which made it even more difficult for Yvonne to stop using them, delaying her skincare success. So, needless to say, we have had our ebbs and flows. Over the years, she would avoid everything I recommended, clear up, only to go back to old habits and break out again.

I never mind having to lecture about what to avoid. We all get comfortable and resume bad habits and need a gentle nudge to remind us how to be great again. Even in your fifties, you can still experience acne if you are continuing the things that cause it. Recently, Yvonne was in for a treatment, and I noticed she was experiencing those old familiar breakouts again. We discovered that a new lip product she had purchased had oils and petroleum as its main ingredients. She discontinued it, and by her follow up visit, she was all clear again. Wooo whoooo, Yvonne! She always comes through a winner.

Client Success Story: Laurie L.

Laurie L. has been my client for seventeen years. Now at the young age of fifty-three, she is still taking amazing care of her skin, and it shows. In her late thirties, when I first met her, her skin was flaw-less. By flawless, I mean a smooth texture, even complexion, and glowing, hydrated, and blemish free skin. Getting facials regularly on a monthly basis was a new thing for Laurie when she first began coming to me. Some people have "good genes," so they believe they have to do very little or nothing to their skin. I disagree with this theory. No matter how great your genes are, gravity will always find residence on one's face eventually and environmental factors that accelerate aging will as well. The best course of action to slow down the process of aging is to get in front of this and care for your skin no matter how flawless it is. And this is what Laurie did. Today at fifty-three, she still looks in her thirties. She is diligent about exercise, drinking her water, eating healthy, and caring for her skin. Even with all she does, she is now experiencing dry skin, and, based on what products she uses for her short and very hip hairdo, she can get a blemish or two as well. From time to time, I give Laurie my lecture about not using fabric softeners, laying off the dairy and caffeine, and wrapping her hair at night. She rolls her eyes and complies. She follows my recommendations, and her skin is then better able to retain moisture for hydration and be breakout free again.

In our fifties, transepidermal water loss is much more common because of menopause and the naturally-occurring changes we experience as we age. So this really requires us to avoid things like caffeine which is a mild diuretic causing the body to eliminate more water. The topical application of skincare products with ingredients such as hyaluronic acid and niacinamide are extremely beneficial during this time to help combat dehydration (transepidermal water loss).

If allergies exist or if medications for high blood pressure are being used, this will cause the skin to be even drier. Laurie has allergies, and as she blossoms forward in age, her allergies have become more aggressive, requiring her to really limit certain things in her diet to help her skin retain its moisture. She is on a full skincare system of topical serums that include her antioxidants, hyaluronic acids, and peptides to keep her skin hydrated and glowing with a youthful appearance.

Tips for Women in Their Fifties

- Focus on exfoliation.
- Eye cream and sunscreen are a must.
- Be sure to use brightening serums, hyaluronic acid, peptides, and antioxidants serums to keep skin healthy and vibrant.
- Focus on a healthy diet and exercise.
- Using a silk pillowcase will also be helpful as cotton absorbs moisture from the skin, and your goal is to stay as hydrated as possible.
- Moisturize to keep skin hydrated and preserved, and use a sunscreen every single day.

Some Simple Tips

- Change linen and face towels weekly and avoid fabric softeners.
- Avoid greasy hair products, gels, mousses, and most leave-in products. Less is best in the hair.
- Make sure to always wrap your hair at night to avoid hair contacting the pillow, which contacts your face.
- Aim for a reasonably healthy, balanced diet.

Why You Need a Separate Eye Cream from Your Moisturizer

Eye creams, when formulated correctly, are targeted treatments. They target the fragile under-eye and upper-eyelid area, stimulating collagen and elastin, which smooths out fine lines and keeps the wrinkles away. Targeted treatments are designed to treat a specific condition or area of concern effectively with more highly concentrated levels of active ingredients. This allows for deeper penetration, helping the skin and cells function the way they were intended to.

Moisturizers are developed to soothe and hydrate at a surface level and seal all our targeted treatments in. They are often formulated with additives for added topical moisture such as emollients, humectants, and squalene, to name a few. These ingredients, by nature, have larger molecules that weigh the thin eyelid area down. Therefore, targeted eye treatments are more ideal for the eye area. They are made with tiny molecules that penetrate deeply, not weighing the skin around the eye down, causing more sagging.

Keep Your Eyes on the Prize

Because the eye area is so delicate, the ingredients used in an effective eye cream or gel is going to be significantly more expensive than a moisturizer. Remember, moisturizers are intended to sit on top of the skin's outermost layer. Choose an eye cream or gel, and ditch your moisturizer around your eyes. Fresh, youthful eyes are the goal!

Let your quest in life be to discover who you are and all the good you are. Your reward will be the gift of purpose.–Maisha

When you rise, be sure to shine. —Maisha

9

SIXTIES SKIN CARE

It's not what you do that makes you phenomenal. It's who you are that does —Maisha

This is the sexy sixties! This is where you say, "Hey, girl! I'm in my sixties and embracing every single piece of me!" By now you've heard that sixty is the new forty, and if you haven't heard, now you have! So dance like you've never danced before. It's a new day! Likely you've embraced your inner sexy, who you are, who you're still becoming, and how amazing you are! And if you haven't, it's time to do so. You have a much better understanding of what true happiness is, and you have a world of wisdom you've waited your entire life for.

I have heard from some women that sixty brings with it a deep shift. That you are preparing for something even more meaningful at this stage. Does this sound like you? You know you aren't as young as you once were, but you don't feel old either. You feel a full life ahead of you, and you are prepared to live it. We all know that time goes by so fast, but this is a great time to take control and slow time down energetically. Slow it down, really. And by slow down, in no way do I mean stop. For those of us full of life, it never stops. There is so much to do, and likely you are doing all the things you have waited many years for! Take deeper breaths, meditate often, and live in each amazing moment as long as you can. Reduce the hustle and bustle as it only speeds time up. You've done enough of that in your life anyway.

So, Really, Slow Down

I want you to think about your eighty-year-old self. Who is she; where is she in life? Invite her to sit and have a cup of coffee, tea, or a cocktail with you and really have a conversation with her. She is only there to listen right now. She won't interrupt. She is incredibly curious about what you have to say, and she desperately wants you to share your deepest thoughts and feelings. What would you tell her? Once you have shared with her, how did it make you feel? Now, I want you to change seats with her.

Imagine your eighty-year-old self wants to speak with you today. She wants to share her deepest thoughts and feelings with you and to give you her best advice. What would she say? And once she has shared, how did that make you feel?

This is something I do from time to time to remember that I am all knowing, and so are you. It's important that we visit our future selves to find perspective. I believe we put a lot of pressure on ourselves about where we should be, what we haven't accomplished, fear about where we are, if we will make it, if we have done enough, all the "what ifs." But our future selves always say, "Girl, don't be afraid. Baby, I have faith in you. You have what it takes to make anything and everything you want possible. It's not too late. I am so happy and at peace right now because of all you were willing to do. Thank you, gorgeous, thank you for taking care of me so I can be living the life I am living right now."

Isn't your future self so kind, gentle, grateful, and incredibly confident? Well, guess what? You are that person now! Whoever that is you see in your future is 100 percent you! All this says to me is that you can rest assured that everything will be just fine. Our thoughts and imagination create not just our present reality but also our future. So, keep creating!

Sixties Skin

You've probably figured out that sixty is not the "old age" you once thought it was. Nope! All is not over. For this reason, it is not a time to be passive about your skin care. You have plenty of years ahead of you to look vibrant and healthy for. You can reverse signs of aging and have amazing skin forever! You will get older, it is inevitable, but you don't ever have to look it!

Your sixties are a time to be serious and intentional about skincare products and a regimen that keeps your skin hydrated and infused with as many nutrients as possible. It is essential to load up on products that hydrate the skin and boost collagen. Sunscreen is always key, as is an eye cream for that delicate eye area. You'll also want to use the right antioxidants, a retinol, peptides, and, of course, exfoliation to help the skin out with cell turnover, which slows over time.

Client Success Story: Carolyn

Carolyn and I met when she was forty-three years old. She is now sixty and looks absolutely fabulous. When I first met Carolyn, she was battling some acne breakouts and hyperpigmentation that her acne had left behind. We worked to clear her acne by having her use ingredients like salicylic, glycolic, kojic, and azelaic acid for her home care and chemical peels and facial treatments during her monthly facial visits. We controlled her acne breakouts and evened out her complexion over time. Carolyn has always been incredibly compliant. Over the years, I have tried various different skincare brands and products to stay current with new developments in science and the industry. Carolyn was always open to experiment and try new things. Clients like Carolyn are always a joy because it gives the esthetician the opportunity to test out products firsthand and get client feedback. Carolyn has always been a trouper which is probably why we are very good friends to this day. I call her my big sister. We have shared so much in my facial room. Laughs, tears, stories, victories, challenges, and, of course, we can't forget...skin care!

It wasn't long after Carolyn and I began working together that she achieved the results she was seeking. As the years went by, although we had controlled her breakouts, she began to develop subtle melasma and extremely sensitive skin which we later identified as eczema. This can occur later in life as the skin matures. Allergies become more aggressive and melasma begins to spike, often due to hormonal shifts within the body. We then needed to change some of her skincare products because some of them, including retinol and glycolic acid, became a bit too stimulating. We put her on a retinol for sensitive skin and switched to lactic acid, added a hyaluronic acid, niacinamide, and, along with some diet changes, her skin normalized. She definitely has to avoid many dietary things now due to her sensitivities including dairy, dairy replacements (such as almond milk, coconut milk, and oat milk), soy, chocolate, and green tea, to name a few. All of this manages to keep her skin normalized, hydrated, and happy.

Client Success Story: Loretta

Loretta has been my client for nineteen of the twenty-one years I have been an esthetician. When we first met, I was a relatively new "esti" at the salon where Loretta had her hair done. She called for an appointment, but since no one was available for the time she wanted, I recommended she have a facial service with me, and when we were done, a stylist would be available for her hair. I offered her a facial instead of her waiting an hour doing nothing. She agreed, and she has been my client since.

Loretta had an advanced condition of melasma, acne, and hyperpigmentation resulting from acne. I worked with her for many years to control the acne and melasma, which would eventually address the acne scarring. For quite some time, it seemed like a vicious cycle. We would clear up her old scars, and new ones would develop. I gave her every treatment I offered, and they were very effective. She used homecare products that included ingredients like glycolic acid, kojic acid, azelaic acid, and hydroquinone, to name a few. I recommended she make some lifestyle changes, such as no sunbathing or washing her face with hot water or driving with her sunroof open. She always complied with all the recommendations I made to her.

The one mystery for a while was her scarring. I would often ask her if she was picking her face, and she would always deny that she was. Intuitively, I knew she was picking. One visit, she came in, and I gently told her that I was certain she was picking and the only way I could help her get rid of the scarring was if she stopped. I told her I needed her to be honest with me. She 'fessed up and admitted she was picking, which I appreciated. We laughed about the secret being out and that now we could really clear her up. I worked with Loretta to create discipline around not picking. Her reason for picking was because the bumps hurt, and she wanted to give her skin relief, so I offered that she could make an emergency appointment for extractions when she felt the urge to pick. She finally stopped picking. Her once aggressive melasma has lightened and faded tremendously due to continued treatments with me, and today, her skin looks amazing.

Although we reversed much of her melasma and hyperpigmentation, she understands that melasma is an incurable condition that can only be controlled, managed, and improved with continued treatments. We continue today with safe, gentle chemical peels and homecare products to keep her skin bright and tight with a healthy glow. At sixty-five years old, no one would ever guess.

Self-love is your investment, return, and reward.

−Maisha

10

SEVENTIES AND BEYOND SKIN CARE

Being intentional about your life, sets the stage for the best performance of your life —Maisha

W elcome, beautiful! This decade marks the beginning of your golden years. A time to kick your feet up and celebrate. A time to throw caution to the wind and do all the things you've been putting off. That professional glam photo shoot, skydiving, hot-air balloon ride, a trip around the world to the places you only dreamed of, finally speaking and actually living your truth out loud. Hey, whatever it is, it's your time to shine and to live big, bold, and fabulous. You've had seventy years, and maybe more, and it's given you wisdom out of this world. Are you sharing it? This is a time to give all the advice you can. Trust me, some younger ears can't wait to absorb all you have experienced and learned. This is the biggest joy in life. To serve and help others become just as fabulous or more than you. Do you agree? I know our experiences aren't just for us. They are to help others have the opportunity for an even better quality of life than we do. This is what we give to others when we are willing to be open, vulnerable, and transparent about what we have experienced. It's why I love biographies and biographical films. I learn and grow so much from other people's experiences. Knowing their challenges and what they overcame always inspires me. It has always been so important for me to know I am not alone in what I have suffered, endured, or even the challenges I've faced in life. It is always that push I need to keep going. This is what you do for us. So please, be the beautiful open book to those that need you.

When I see women that are seventy-plus who are so full of life, I want to run to seventy. I love the confidence, grace, and empowerment I sense from you. If you aren't experiencing these things, I encourage you to start engaging friendships with women like this that are your age. It isn't too late to turn this around. Take control of your life and live it to the fullest. If you are this energetic seventy-plus-year-old, please be willing to share your light with someone that needs it. Spread your joy and make it contagious.

Time to Give It All You Got

While enjoying this decade and beyond, don't forget about your skin. It's depending on you to give it continued, dedicated attention and time. Facials are still important. As are manicures, pedicures, massages, or whatever makes you feel great and cared for. Your daily homecare regimen for your skin should be a piece you don't leave out. This ensures you are getting proper exfoliation and hydration to pamper your delicate skin, keeping it supple and healthy. At this time in life, you don't want to be too aggressive with your skin. Do not over exfoliate as the skin is much thinner and more fragile. Capillaries are easier to break, causing redness. This is not a time to give up on your SPF or serums such as your antioxidants and peptides. Using a heavier moisturizer is generally necessary as the skin is likely drier due to transepidermal water loss, which is common during this age. The skin has a more difficult time retaining water, so it evaporates quickly and easily. So pump up on a hyaluronic acid serum and a rich moisturizer. A hydrating sleep mask used overnight will also help with moisture retention. This is the most important skin of your life. This is the skin you have spent so many years thinking about, wondering what is best for it, having sleepless nights over, investing in, and I am certain so much more, so take really good care of it.

Client Success Story: Viola D.

Viola D., started coming to me for facial services ten years ago when she was sixty-three. She was very healthy. She exercised regularly, ate really well, drank plenty of water, and took care of her skin. The esthetician who had previously cared for her skin had recently gone out of business, and Viola was referred to me. When we began working together, I was so impressed with how well she looked for her age. I noticed she was developing melasma, and we began working to fade, reverse, and slow down the progression of the condition. Vi, as I call her, has always been compliant, although at the time, she preferred to keep her facial treatments and home care very basic. We started off by only doing basic facials, and she only used basic essentials for her home care which were her cleanser, toner, moisturizer, and sunscreen. There reached a point about four years ago when she was sixty-eight years old that I noticed her melasma advancing, as well as her skin showing signs of aging that I was confident we could reverse. I recommended this would be a great time to advance her facial treatments and home care beyond the basics. I began doing chemical peels and oxygen treatments as well as adding peptides, retinol, and antioxidants to her home care. Vi's skin turned around for the better rapidly. Impression lines smoothed out, melasma faded tremendously, and her texture became firmer. This is why I say it is never too late for skin care.

Often there are clients who express they want a simple homecare system, and they don't want to invest much on facial treatments; however, once they give it a try and see the drastic improvements, they change their minds and feel it's all worth it just as Vi did! Today, at the ripe young age of seventy-three years old, Vi looks so youthful and healthy. Skin care and self-care always!

Client Success Story: Elen H.

Elen H., now seventy-eight, began coming to me when she was sixty-nine years old. If I didn't trust and know skin care in the way that I do, I would have had a lot of doubt that there was anything I, or anyone else for that matter, could do to help her skin improve. She was certain that she had damaged and neglected her skin for so long that there was no way to improve it with facial treatments and skincare products. She told me her only reason for getting facials was because they felt good, and she wanted to support a small business. That tickled me, though I kept the humor of her comment to myself. I was so excited to take on the challenge to not only impress her with results but to also feed my ego. I love seeing skin change before my eyes. I get to pat myself on the back and say, "Maisha—you go, girl!"

Elen was not only experiencing severe dryness and dehydration due to allergies and medication but also melasma, advanced sun damage, environmental stress, a rough, leathery texture, and deep-set wrinkles. I rolled up my sleeves and got to work. I first recommended that she discontinue coffee and any caffeine immediately. The high blood pressure medications she was on were diuretics, so the coffee made matters worse causing further dryness and leaving the skin lifeless-looking with a dark and greyish cast. Dehydration causes melasma to look even darker. I advised her to avoid all dairy and dairy replacements and, of course, switch her laundry detergent to a free and clear detergent with absolutely no added softeners which are full of chemicals that also exacerbate the problem for sensitive skin such as Elen's. Because of her fragile, sensitive, aged skin as well as what I knew about her lifestyle and habits (which were not conducive to advanced chemical peels which would have served her better), I selected a very gentle approach to treating her skin. Instead of chemical peels, I selected vitamin C, oxygen, and enzyme treatments, to name a few. Her homecare products consisted of brighteners, lighteners, and tighteners. Elen was pretty compliant. It was difficult for her to cut the coffee out, but she managed to eventually do it, and guess whose skin turned around and improved? You guessed it! Elen's and I am so proud of her. Certainly, had Elen taken better care of her skin years ago, her skin would be far healthier and clear today; however, starting when she did allows her to have an even clearer complexion today, tomorrow, and beyond.

Tips for Women in Their Seventies and Beyond

- Treat your skin ever so delicately like a flower. It deserves to be pampered so be gentle.
- This is a perfect time to moisturize several times a day. It's the beauty secret of Lena Horne and Joan Collins. They both said they moisturized several times a day to keep wrinkles away. This is truly the best-kept secret to healthy skin at this age.
- Use brighteners, peptides, and antioxidant serums to keep the skin bright, reverse signs of aging, and keep the skin looking as youthful as possible.

- Eat healthy and take walks often to help with blood circulation.
- Invest in a silk pillowcase. Cotton absorbs moisture from the skin while silk helps the skin to retain its moisture.
- Apply a sunscreen every single day.
- Daily facial exercises will help to firm the skin and smooth fine lines and wrinkles.

Give You and Your Skin Your Best. It Will Be One Thing You Will Never Regret!

When writing this book, I dreamt of you holding it and feeling empowered not just to care for your skin in a more intentional way but to also go within and care for the inner you in the most amazing way possible. I wanted you to know you aren't alone along this journey, and at every phase in your life, know that I, along with many other women, are energetically walking with you, cheering you on to be the *amazing* you that you were created to be. Self-care is the greatest gift we can give ourselves, and that means we focus on mind, body, and spirit always. Skin care is a major piece of self-care, and I hope you have been inspired through this book to give even more special attention to your skin. Whether you are thirteen or ninety-three, love on you in the deepest, truest way possible, and you will face this world glowing from the inside out! Skin care always!

You can always get more tips and inspiration by visiting my website at SkinbyMaisha.com or on social media. On Instagram and Facebook, find me at Skin by Maisha.

The relationship with yourself has a beginning, middle, and forever. Fall in love with you. —Maisha

A NOTE TO YOU

This project is a dream come true. Since I was a child, I imagined myself as an author, and to actually see this project come to life brings tears to my eyes. This book is real live proof that I am strong because writing this book wasn't easy. Although I always wanted to write a book, I never imagined it would be my purpose. I often daydreamed of being an author, and many times, it felt so real. You've heard the expression, "If your mind can conceive and believe, it can achieve"? For me, this certainly proved to be true.

Writing stretched me to do what I was put on this earth for: to live out my purposes. (Yes, I believe we have more than one purpose.) I believe that is our chief goal on this earth...to live out our purpose. Not everyone does, often because fear and the threat that it will be too hard defeats them. I am here to tell you nothing is "too" hard. Sure, things are often hard, but there's nothing you can't do when you set your mind to it. Setting a nonnegotiable intention to live out your purpose is a sure-fire way to make sure you do. Meditate on your purpose day and night. Continue to even if that means continuing to go within yourself to ask what that purpose is. I mentioned we have many purposes to live out in this life. It is important to stay open to receive each call to action from our Higher Source.

As well as multiple purposes, I believe we all have stories in us, and although not everyone is interested in sharing them, I am so grateful to all those who have been willing to be storytellers. Their stories were my road map to becoming braver and vulnerable enough to begin to share mine. I have always been one to serve in the best way I can. My thoughts have always been, "How can I be of service to others in a way that feeds my soul?" Skin care was definitely the answer. I knew I had to be more transparent than ever to help other women reach their goals. When I first knew that intuitively, it confused me. First of all, God knows how private I am, yet helping is what I love to do so sharing my life was unavoidable. And the still small voice inside me wouldn't go away and eventually got louder and louder until about a year ago it said, "Write a book about skin care and your life experiences." This message couldn't have been clearer at a time in my life when so much was changing. The message finally made sense. Which is another thing that let me know that this was a purpose, a calling. The clarity came. As afraid as I was to take on this challenge, I sucked it up and agreed to move forward. Because for me, there was no other choice.

To know that you'd be holding and reading this book was all I thought of as I was writing it. I saw you on the other side of this project. Thank you for waiting for me. Now I'm waiting for you to live out what your purposes are and have a no-compromise approach about it. My goal is that you see yourself in every page as I see myself in every woman. I wrote this for you. This project is for every woman living, who has lived before me and will after me. I am a reflection of you, and you have inspired me every step of the way.

On the other side of fear, you will find all the strength you need to make it through. It's waiting for you. —Maisha

NOTES

3. Acne-Prone Skin

1. For more information about ingredients to avoid, go to – ewg.org

ACKNOWLEDGMENTS

To PCA, Thank you for all your support over these years. Our partnership is one which I cherish. Thank you for continuing to provide stellar products that have helped support not just my work but also the faces I love and care so much about. Thank you for being innovative and remaining on the cutting edge of skin care and science, providing a vast array of products catering to all skin types and conditions. I appreciate you so much!

To my life coach Finnegan Mwape, The Universe has a way of aligning things perfectly and you are alignment-perfection at its finest. Thank you for magically appearing in my life and pushing me when the world and the tasks it presented felt so challenging and unachievable. Thank you for helping me see my life's map more clearly and coaching me along this journey of my life. You were needed and I appreciate you beyond words.

Thank you, Catherine, Carolyn, and Ms. Donna for allowing me to interview you for the decades I have not experienced yet. Sharing your experiences with me gave me all the inspiration I needed to write those chapters, and I am beyond grateful for your time, love, and confidence in me. Most of all, I am grateful for your friendship. These years I've had you in my life have been a true gift, and I know God allowed our paths to cross purposely. This journey has been so much easier because of you.

To Jessica, my bright and rising superstar, my bonus daughter, my cheerleader, my friend. You are not just a valuable member of the team. You are so much more. Thank you for being my other right hand. I am so blessed to have you in my life, and I'm grateful for all you do professionally and personally for me. This project would not have been able to happen without you doing all that you did to give me the peace of mind and time I needed to write this book. Thank you from the bottom of my heart. My prayer is that all things great shower you ceaselessly and abundantly. You are so magnificently deserving.

To each and every client I used as a case study in this book, I thank you so much for this opportunity.

Not just the opportunity to write about our experiences, but I also thank you for trusting your skin in my hands all these years. I am so proud of the compliance, discipline, and patience that it took for you to gain the results you were seeking. You proved my theory of teamwork truly making the dream work!

To every esthetician using your gift to improve lives through skin care, I salute you! This work is not easy, and there are many days I know you feel a lot of pressure to be great, but remember that you are, so don't put so much pressure on yourself doubting that fact. I know there are days you wonder if you're doing enough and if you know enough. Be kind and gentle to yourself. Allow yourself time to unplug, relax, and restore. Your clients want you to take care of you too, and you are so deserving of it. There is always more to learn. No one person knows everything. Your clients don't expect you to know the answer to everything; they just expect you to have the resources to get the answer and remember...you can. You are super resourceful, and there is so much support out here for you. I want you to win! Stay true to yourself by being the amazing person you are, believing in yourself, and giving your clients the best service you possibly can. No one expects you to do any more or any less than that. Big hugs, love, and success to you.

To my host of family and friends (you know who you are), thank you for loving me every step of the way. Your support has been a gift, and I couldn't do any of this without you. You are my personal cheerleaders, always in my corner cheering me on, and for that I am forever grateful. I prayed for true friends. I spent countless hours imagining what that would look like, and I was blessed with exactly what I visioned—family and friends who love and support me unconditionally. Family and friends that I can be vulnerable and completely transparent with, that don't judge me, just continue to love and encourage me. For this I thank you, from the bottom of my heart.

To my editor, author coach, and friend, Diane Riis, you and I are simply synchronicity at its finest! Our meeting each other couldn't have come at a more perfect time. Thank you for all the hours of talks and encouragement when I felt like turning back and that there was no way I could make this project happen. You refused to let me give up, and I can't begin to thank you enough. All the tears shed and heartfelt talks were the driving force I needed to make this project happen. You are a manifested dream come true. You are an angel, Diane. You made work feel like play. Thank you for your ear, wise and gentle words, patience, and most of all, your time and love. I love you, my friend.

AUTHOR BIO/PROGRAM OFFERING

Maisha Pulliam has been serving as an Esthetician and Accountability Coach for her clients for over 20 years. She works with teens and adults who have skin concerns, women who want to reverse the signs of aging and anyone who wants to relax and be pampered. But her work is so much deeper than skin care.

Maisha has been fascinated with beauty and all things related from an early age. Suffering from acne as a child, she was driven to learn all she could about skin care and the business of esthetics. Her empathy for those struggling with their appearance and self-confidence makes her work incredibly powerful. Now Maisha shares her method and philosophy with her readers, but that's just the beginning.

If you are ready to find peace, improve your sense of self-worth and live a happier life, Maisha invites you to explore her **Personal Transformation Coaching** program where she will help you learn to love yourself inside and out. You can find out more at... SkinbyMaisha.com/MaiEarIsHere

If you are an esthetician who wants to help women look and feel radiant inside and out, Maisha has customized a one-of-a-kind program just for you. In her **Esthetician's Personal and Business Transformation Coaching** you will learn to be a truly transformational skin care expert. Her specialized coaching will let you take your career and business to a whole new level and you will become the woman you are destined to be.

"There is a world of beauty that needs healing." - Maisha

Are you going to be part of the transformation?

You can find out more at... SkinbyMaisha.com/MaiEarIsHere

"I've come to know Maisha beyond being just my
esthetician. Maisha is not only a mother and friend,
but a life coach, a listening ear, a cheerleader, a goal
getter, and an inspiration. Of course she expects you
to leave better than you came regarding your skincare experience, BUT she also wants you to leave
better than you came from the inside out. Some of
my most joyous moments are when Maisha is
sharing her pearls of wisdom, or when she is being
extremely transparent and sharing her personal
experiences, so you don't feel as though you're the
only person experiencing life alone. Her stories
always captivate me, because she speaks with such
clarity, compassion, animation and understanding of
what life is teaching her. Maisha is not just a person
wandering through life. She is a seeker of knowledge
and understanding.

Maisha is a woman who feels everything deeply and
intuitively, which allows her to have so much
empathy for her sisters and brothers. No bullsh*t,
Maisha is magic and magical. She is the tangible

feeling and form of "magic". She has this way of making you feel sincerely seen and cared for. There have been many days when I came for Beauty Maintenance Treatment feeling tired, depleted or unmotivated. After experiencing Maisha's energy, listening to her stories, which always have a message, or just having a candid conversation that somehow leads us to dig deeper...I swear to God, I leave her feeling motivated, refreshed and energized. Magic.

Maisha and I talk about how we must have known each other in another life because we naturally "click." We have shared our hearts, thoughts, ideas, cares and concerns with one another without judgement and in confidence. That's rare. I appreciate her and love her more than she knows!

I am ABSOLUTELY ECSTATIC to continue to be able to witness Maisha walk in her purpose and share her gifts. Her heart posture, kindness, and humility alone are a testament to why God will continue to bless her in ALL that she does."

—Yemaya Teague, Owner of Legacy Eleven, wife and mother

* * *

"Growing up my skin was my worst enemy. I vividly remember when acne hit me in sixth grade. It was horrible AND I was a picker, which made it worse. I remember looking at my skin and wanting to die or put a paper bag over my head. There were times when I did not even want to go to school. I had dark spots all through junior high and high school and I always dreaded picture day. My nicknames were 'pizza face,' 'spotty the dog' and many more. As I got older it got a little better, but the breakouts would still come from time to time.

Fast-forward to getting accepted into a fast-paced radiology program. That's when it went downhill. My face looked exactly how it did in high school. I was so embarrassed that I began searching for someone to get this skin under control. I found Maisha and what sold me was the pictures my cousin showed me of one of Maisha's clients. The "before and after" convinced me and I finally booked my appointment.

When I first met Maisha I was a bit intimidated, not by her so much but just by the new journey, the cost and the question, "Will this really work?" I tried someone else before and it didn't go the way I wanted it to. Let's just say ya girl was a little bit trau-matized. Maisha has a very strong personality, and she has knowledge and passion for skincare but at first I did not trust her. We laugh about this now, but I would go against everything she would tell me. She was always so patient and kind with me. Once she asked me what kind of lotion I was using, and I LOVED this lotion. She kept telling me it was the cause of my breakouts and I would not listen. I would say she didn't know what she was talking about, even though I was seeing good results from working with her. So, for a week I did what she said. She was right! I had no more breakouts. From that day forward whatever she tells me to do, I do. After being her faithful client for almost two years my skin has never looked or felt better. I get compli-ments wherever I go. So many people have gone to see Maisha because they see the difference in my skin. But the most rewarding feeling about my skin care journey is that I can leave the house without wearing makeup and I feel so confident! The old Alecia would NEVER walk out the house without makeup with all those dark marks. Now I don't even like makeup anymore. I just went to a concert makeup- free and it was the best feeling ever.

Maisha you are truly a skin angel. I am so blessed to have found you. The confidence you've given me has exceeded my expectations and I am forever grateful.

All I had to do was let my guard down, trust you and do the work. Maisha does not care about your money. She cares about the results. I know this because one day she was so honest with me—and I'll never forget this—she said, 'Alecia you are paying me all this money and every time you pick we take a step backwards. That is basically wasting your money.'

And she was right. She could've kept taking my money but she truly does care about her client's skin. That's what keeps her in business. From that day on I stopped picking because I sure don't have money to waste. Not only has she become my esthetician, but a great friend and I love her dearly."

—Alecia Alexander, Radiologic Technologist

"Before I started seeing Maisha I saw three derma-tologists and tried vast amounts of over -the-counter skin care products and home remedies. At one point I stopped searching for a solution and accepted my skin for what it was: bad skin. I was embarrassed when I went in for my first facial because oftentimes I was judged. People thought my hygiene was poor or that I didn't care about my skin, but that wasn't the case. I didn't know what I was doing wrong or where to begin. I was hopeless. When I met Maisha she was delightful: a woman of great character and charm. I immediately trusted her with my skin. Maisha helped me realize that investing in my skin was worth every cent but she never pressured me into making extreme purchases. She worked with me every step of the way. She shared tips with me and would graciously hold my face and say "Aliyah, you have to stop," referring to whatever bad habit I couldn't let go of. I never felt insulted or offended, I knew she was on my side; I knew she wanted my skin to heal. Maisha became more than my esthetician, Maisha became family. She would tell me about her childhood, her grandmother, her passion, and her baby Blaique; she loves her some Blaique. I felt honored to listen to her obstacles, her triumphs, her dreams and most importantly her faith. Maisha and I met because of her profession and my need for clear skin, but we connected because of our spirit. On numerous occasions I left the Spa with answers I'd been seeking for months. I didn't know I'd receive a facial and words of wisdom simultaneously. Maisha has helped me heal immensely, inside and out. I am inspired by Maisha, what I value the most is her genuine love and appreciation for life and overall peace. If you're lucky enough to meet her, embrace every second of it. Maisha is supportive, honest, stylish, beautiful, intelligent, and exciting to be around! Thank you for your services, thank you for your support, thank you for your love, thank you for your vulnerability—thank you for everything! Love you always."

—Aliyah Bey, Nutritionist and personal trainer

"I have had the pleasure of having Maisha as my esthetician for over 5 years. Her gift is without question her ability to care for you from the inside out. Not only has she advised me on how to care for my skin, but also my diet and other daily habits. Her knowledge is impeccable. During one visit, Maisha was able to identify a skin disorder before my dermatologist diagnosed me. Her willingness to enlighten and educate shows how much she is invested in her clients.

In full transparency, I have not only benefited from Maisha as an esthetician, but I've also benefited from her superpowers: her wisdom and heart. While her hands are working, her heart is healing. We have laughed, cried, prayed and celebrated moments that have made a lasting impression. That service comes with a small cost..... you have to be open to receive.

Whether you are beginner or master at self- care and self -love, I hope you allow Maisha to help guide you on your journey. This book is a reflection of Maisha's heart. It is so full that it cannot be confined to a one- hour treatment. This is the over-flow from Maisha's heart that will help transform you from the inside out. Be ready!"

—*Michelle Webber MA, wife, mother, daughter, sister, friend*

* * *

"In all of the years that I've known Maisha, I can honestly call her one of the dopest women that I know. As her client, I have known her to go above and beyond to provide intentional and consistent service. As a businesswoman, I admire her drive and dedication to her art; and as one woman to another, I've taken note of how she walks in grace, integrity and so much class. I can testify to her beautiful spirit and the wisdom in her words. I've been fortunate enough to gather many valuable gems from her throughout the years and now I am excited for her to share all of her gifts, wisdom, and talent with the world. Cheers to another chapter, with love!"

—*MarQuita Petties, Owner of That's My Jam Company*

* * *

"My skin journey with Maisha began on my birthday, I don't remember which. Initially, I sought her services to support her as a black women entrepreneur and as a friend from high school whose shine I had hoped to celebrate. What I didn't know on that birthday was how much of a gift she was giving to me; the gift of who she is as a human being, the gift of Sista friendship, and the gift of loving myself through loving my skin.

Maisha's own skin is her testimony. It had noticeably gone from adolescent acne-flawed to the glorious glow of Maisha's current skin-goddessness. Whatever she was dishing out, I wanted to soak it in! So, for my birthday in whatever year that was, I treated myself to a facial. Before that day, I had been satisfied that my over-the-counter face wash and cocoa butter regimen was sufficient. I had convinced myself that my grandmother's good genes and my deep melanin cover had done its best to protect me from the sun and all of the fried foolishness that might show up within my pores. On her table, my face in her hands, Maisha turned my head, scrutinized my skin and said, 'You have always had pretty skin. And it looks really good.'

I smiled. But before I could pat myself on the back, she continued, 'but when you are ready for it to look GREAT, you'll do what I'm telling you to do.'

She ran off a short list of grocery items I needed to stop consuming and a robust list of skin changing things that have absolutely made the difference in my life and to my skin. I swear by Maisha's advice and her products, and I am grateful to benefit from all of her gifts, her wit and wisdom, her vibrant personality, her expertise, and her generosity of love. All of it comes through in her service to protect and preserve the skin we are in."

—Shia Shabazz Smith, Writer and educator

"My first experience with having a skin regimen happened when I was about thirty years old. Two beautiful elderly sisters named Elaine and Elizabeth gave me a gift with skincare products in it. I pulled the gift out of the bag and they both said, 'This is really a good product for your skin.'

I looked at how well dressed they were that day (which was the norm for them) and how beautiful their skin was during that season in their lives. I used these products through my thirties, forties, and into my fifties. However, when I began going through the change also known as menopause, I experienced hot flashes, sleepless nights, moodiness, and skin with no glow, and unevenness. I thought that it was just one more thing to deal with while going through the change of life. Yet one day, while discussing skin care, someone suggested I consider getting a facial on a regular basis. She felt that it might help my skin come alive again. It was during this time that my daughter Kendra was going to Skin by Maisha. She said, 'Mama you should go see Maisha. She gives facials but she specializes in skin care.'

I took my daughter's advice and I went to Skin by Maisha once a month for skin care.

After a while, by using the products that Maisha recommended I began to see a positive change in my skin. People began to tell me how pretty and healthy my skin looked. I couldn't believe it at first. When I was younger I did not get compliments like I do now. Maisha has a gift for helping your skin blossom during any season in your life. For example, a couple of years ago I was diagnosed with stage one breast cancer. I would go on early morning walks and pray; I watched my diet, and I continued to keep my skin care appointments. At one appointment I recall Maisha saying, 'Whatever it is that you've been doing, your skin loves it.'

I love how Misha is so professional, but also kind and understanding as well. She has this unique way of looking at your skin and many times being able to tell if you may be having skin issues due to over-indulging in dairy products or just too much caffeine. I am so proud of her. I am also thankful that she has written a book that will inspire people to love the skin that they are in. I consider her a woman with a gift from God to help many people deal with skin issues at any age. She has helped three generations in my family to have healthy skin: my daughters, my granddaughter and me. I am so blessed and honored to love and know her."

—*Reverend Dale Roberts, Author of Picking Up the Pieces of a Broken Heart and I've Got Those Holiday Blues*

"My journey with *Skin by Maisha* started in my teens, and I am now in my late 30s. It's been a long time since I felt comfortable and confident in my own skin. Maisha has taught me how to manage my skin from the inside out by educating me on how my diet affects my skin and which products/facials to include in my skincare regimen. My monthly facials are now a part of my self-care practice. I don't miss an appointment and I make sure to stay consistent by scheduling out my appointments for the year.

Aside from being a skincare guru, Maisha is an amazing woman with a beautiful aura. My facial sessions are often therapy/life coach sessions. Maisha not only gives me skincare advice but she has also given me advice on life in general. I look forward to my facial sessions because I know I will leave my appointment with a glow and a new outlook on life.

Ladies invest in yourself, add Skin by Maisha to your skincare regimen, if you look good, you will feel good."

– Starr Dixon, Practice Support Advisor for Hill Physicians Medical Group

"Maisha Pulliam of Skin by Maish is a gem that shines bright in more than one area!

The last few years I've been blessed by this woman of high caliber both physically, mentally and spiritually. An experience with Skin by Maisha is an encounter of excellence, respect, heightened gratitude and peace! My face care took a turn for the worse and Maisha literally brought me back to healthy skin, and a healthy mindset on pursuing a better me!!

She is a life coach with healing hands and a gift that keeps on giving!! One of the bay's gems, she's known throughout this country for her beautiful spirit, healing hands and professionalism!

I would recommend Maisha over and over again because it's rare you find excellence and style in human form like her!! Thank you for being a friend and esthetician!!"

—India Little, Kaiser Permanente Executive Assistant to NCAL Senior Vice Presidents of Hospital and Health Plan Operations

"I started going to Maisha nearly 15 years ago to treat my acne and dry skin. Little did I know she would not only have a positive impact on my skin, but also on me as a person. Over the years Maisha has seen me grow into an adult and I have seen her business continue to grow and at every phase Maisha has poured wisdom and kindness into me.

Maisha is a passionate person. She is passionate about family, friends, food, and fashion. That same passion can be seen and felt with the well being of her clients. Maisha goes beyond caring for your skin and cares for you as a person.

Every appointment I have had with Maisha has left me with advice, a smile, and a glow. What Maisha pours into to your skin flows to your soul and it shows. It's a privilege to be a client and friend of Maisha's."

—Jasmine Barlow, Kaiser Senior Account Manager

Made in the USA
Las Vegas, NV
12 November 2021

34282277R00115